To Malcolm

ALONG OLYMPIC ROAD

Along Olympic Road

FOSTER HEWITT

THE RYERSON PRESS ~ TORONTO

PRINTED AND BOUND IN CANADA
BY THE RYERSON PRESS, TORONTO

CONTENTS

ALONG OLYMPIC ROAD

Early
Canadian
Champions

CHAPTER 1

On the back steps of a farm home two old-time champions sat leisurely on a summer evening and recalled the great athletes of their boyhood.

"Do you remember Tom Longboat, the Indian runner?" Jack Curry inquired from his friend Ed Cross.

"Indeed I do," was the enthusiastic response. "In fact, I saw him start in his first big race. He was then only seventeen years old, long and lean, and had never run a race over two miles in his life. He was from the Caledonia Reserve, you know."

"What was the race, Ed?"

"It was the annual Hamilton-Around the Bay marathon held on Thanksgiving Day. In fact, after all these years, it still is," he added.

1

"I remember it as if it was yesterday," Ed recalled. "In that long line of starters, there were the best distance runners in America, and the only fellow who seemed out of place was young Tom Longboat.

"I didn't go out on the road with them," Ed continued. "But every little while a report would come back. 'Longboat ahead by 100 yards; Longboat leading by 250 yards; Longboat now 400 yards in front.'"

"It was just too bad," the experts were saying. "This race will kill the young Indian. He needs good handlers. They should never have let him get so far in front. He's running his race in the first half. He probably won't even finish."

"And did he?" Jack interrupted.

"The farther he went, the greater was his lead," Ed related. "When I saw him coming down the road to the finish line, he was loping along at the same pace that he started—and just as fresh, too."

"Was his time good?"

"Good!" Ed laughed. "It was perfect. I remember, as Longboat finished, the timers stopped their watches, looked at them, turned away, shook their heads, then hustled over to other timers. They huddled and smiled, for their watches all agreed. Young Tom, in his first race off the Reserve, running on rubber-soled shoes for the second time in his life, had not only won the famous race, but had also made a new record."

"How would Longboat have compared with Sherring?" Jack asked his old friend.

"Hard to say," Ed thought. "I think Bill was a little over his peak when Tom was just beginning to

2

come. But Sherring won the Olympic marathon and Longboat didn't do that."

"That's right," Jack recalled. "That was in 1906 at Athens. As I remember, Sherring went to Athens with three other Olympians—Elwood Hughes, Don Linden and Ed Archibald."

"The race started around three o'clock, from the huge marble stadium," Ed related. "It went out over tough roads and hills; and it wasn't until nearly six o'clock, when a little runner wearing a green shamrock on his white jersey, with a battered old fedora on his head, entered the stadium and continued to run down the track. Then a surprising incident happened."

"What was that?" Jack interrupted.

"Well! just as Sherring started down the stretch, a tall, athletic man, dressed in smart blue serge suit, with lots of gold braid on his sleeves and on his peaked cap, hustled across the track and continued stride for stride with the Canadian until he crossed the finish line."

"Didn't anyone interfere?" Jack asked.

"It was good they didn't," Ed chuckled. "That stranger was Prince George of Greece and he was honouring the victor as he accompanied him to the tape."

"Wasn't Sherring the first Canadian to be an Olympic champion?" Jack inquired.

"Most folks, would say so," Ed agreed. "But that isn't right. The truth is that Canada's first Olympic winner was a Montreal policeman named Desmarteau."

"That's correct," his friend recalled. "I remember him. In fact, there were two Desmarteau brothers. They were big and strong. They could compete all day and still be fresh. Between them they could get enough points to win a meet for the Montreal forces. But I didn't know one of them was an Olympic champion," he added.

"Yes! it was Etienne who won our first gold medal," Ed remembered. "He went to St. Louis in 1904 and beat the huge American Whales, as they called them, in the 56-pound weight. He tossed the boulder more than thirty-four feet, and he had to be good to finish ahead of those New York policemen."

"Would you say that Sherring, Longboat and Desmarteau were Canada's best athletes, Ed?"

"No! I wouldn't go that far, Jack," his crony replied. "But it does seem surprising to me that in these times there are so few Canadians who can go into top company in running, jumping or throwing, and make a good showing."

"In our day, Jack," Ed continued, "there were a dozen fellows who were champions at home or abroad. There was Bobby Kerr, who won the Olympic 200-metres dash in London. There was George Orton who won United States titles in a flock of races from the mile up. There was Harry Gill and George Gray. Gray won the American shot-putting championship more than ten times and he was so far ahead of his generation that his best mark wasn't passed for nearly thirty years."

"You knew Walter Knox, of course," Jack inquired.

"Knew him!" exclaimed Ed Cross. "Everybody knew Walter. He was, pound-for-pound, the best track athlete that Canada ever knew. And did he have what

4

they call colour! He was a real prankster, always fooling somebody."

"I remember him telling about the time he visited an American university track where the coach was handling his big team. Did I ever tell you about it, Jack?"

"No! Go ahead," his friend encouraged.

"Well! Knox, looking for some fun, went over to the coach and explained, 'I'm a marathon runner, and a stranger in town. Would you mind if I jogged around your track?'"

"Go ahead," the coach answered.

Knox trotted a few laps, then strolled across to the infield where the coach was instructing the shot-putters. Knox waited a short while, looked very interested, then said to the coach, "I've done a little weight-throwing. Would you mind if I tossed one for you?"

"Don't bother me," the coach answered sharply. "You said you were a marathon runner. Now get away from here."

But Knox continued his pleading and finally to get rid of him was given the shot. Awkwardly, he fingered the big ball, took a couple of hops, and tossed it about thirty feet. The puny effort brought only laughs of derision from athletes and spectators. However, a few minutes later, Knox was back again.

"Coach," he began, "I've been listening to you. Your stuff is good. I see what was wrong with me. Give me another chance and I'll surprise you."

"No!" was the curt response. "You're a nuisance. You're wasting my time. Get away to your track."

"Tell you what I'll do, coach," Knox came back,

5

"give me one more try. If I don't beat the distance made by your best man, I'll give you a new hat."

The coach was on the spot and when his athletes dared him to accept the challenge, he finally gave in, and rolled the shot to Knox.

Walter, always an actor, posed carefully in the whitewashed circle, then told the laughing spectators to step well back or he would hit them. They jeered and defied him.

"All right," shouted Walter. "Stay there and I'll heave it over your heads."

Expertly, he fingered the shot, balanced it close to his shoulder, hopped, reversed and heaved. Over the heads of the gasping onlookers, the ball soared and landed close to forty-seven feet away.

The amazed athletes crowded around Walter as the coach squeezed through. "What did you say your name was?" he asked.

"I didn't say," Walter answered, "but it's Knox."

"Walter Knox?" laughed the coach. "I might have known you weren't a marathon runner. You better stay around here a couple of days and tell us all you know."

"Yes, sir, Knox was quite a fellow," Ed continued. "Do you remember the afternoon he won five Canadian championships? He was a very cocky athlete and I was running in the 100 yards race that day. While we were digging our starting holes, Walter got off the mark, came along the line, and chuckled, 'You fellows better get together and decide who's going to be second.'"

"Yes! I agree with you. Knox could do everything and do it well," Jack remarked. "They told me that

6

four timers once clocked him over 100 yards and their watches stopped at nine and two-fifth seconds. I raced against him when he did nine and three-fifths and he beat me five yards."

"He was a pretty good jumper, too, Jack," Ed recalled. "I used to clear twelve feet in the pole-vault regularly and it was generally good enough to win the Canadian championship. That was high around 1908. But one day, after winning the broad jump and the high jump, this Knox came over to the pole-vault and didn't stop until he cleared twelve feet six inches.

"In my opinion, Jack," Ed continued, "Walter was the greatest athlete Canada ever produced, and it wasn't much surprise to me when he went over to Manchester, England, and won six victories in eight events to become the world's best professional."

"Yes, Ed, we had some real competitors between 1900 and 1910," Jack recalled with pride. "Remember George Goulding. He was originally a runner, then he became interested in walking and before he finished he held the world's record for the mile walk. Somewhere around six minutes and a half. That was really fast. And at one time he was also the record holder for two, three and four miles and he wound up by winning the 10,000 metres Olympic walk at Stockholm."

"In those days," Ed boasted to his friend, "you had to beat a Canadian before you could call yourself a world's champion runner, jumper or weight-thrower. But that isn't so today, Jack. How do you account for it? Have the other countries improved or have we slipped?"

Dave Learns About Weight-Throwing

CHAPTER 2

While Jack and Ed were reliving those years when Canadian track and field athletes were world famous, a couple of young teen-age lads came galloping across the fields towards the house. As the panting runners pursued a zigzagging course, Grandfather Cross explained, "When my son, Jim, went overseas, I promised him that if anything happened, I would look after Mary and the lad. Dave has been a good boy. Going to be a nice size, too."

Then, turning to the two lads as they slumped on the ground, the grandfather looked at the boy and said, "Dave, I'd say you have the shoulders of a weight man. Maybe you could putt the shot, throw the hammer, or even hurl a discus."

"What are those things, grandpa?" the youngster inquired. "I never even heard of them."

"The discus, Dave, is one of sports oldest implements," his grandfather explained. "More than 2,500 years ago when the Ancient Greek Games began in the sacred valley of Olympia, the events were all runs."

"How long were those races, grandpa?" Dave asked.

"At first, they were just one length of the course and the distance was called a stade. A stade was about 210 yards in our distances."

"I guess that's where we got our word stadium, grandpa?"

"Yes! That's true, Dave," his grandfather continued. "Well! then they increased distances to two stades, and later they ran several stades."

"But what about the discus, Mr. Cross?" Dave's friend Allan inquired.

"Oh, yes! Allan, us old fellows do wander, don't we?" laughed the veteran. "After the ancient Olympics had been going for eighty years, they were held every fourth one you know, the Greeks introduced a pentathlon contest. This pentathlon was for all-round competition and one of the five events was throwing a discus. So it's one of our oldest sports, and to the Greeks was the most important of all."

"What does a discus look like, grandpa?" Dave asked.

"A discus, son, is the shape of a couple of inverted saucers if they were cemented together on their rims. A discus has a metal ring with a diameter close to nine inches. Inside this rim is a wooden body with a brass

9

plate in the centre. The weight is a little under four and a half pounds."

"How do they throw it, Mr. Cross?" Allan asked.

"The discus is thrown from inside a white circle just over eight feet in diameter. Styles vary with each athlete, but mostly the discus is held flat in the palm of the hand with the tips of the fingers curling over the edges to give a good grip. In the style I prefer the thrower then stands at the rear of the circle, facing to the back. The athlete then spins on the ball of his left foot, and lands on his right foot in a crouched position. As his body whirls around, the right arm swings out and the discus is hurled into the air."

"It seems a very hard event to me, grandpa. How far do they throw it?" Dave inquired.

"In my day, the best discus thrower in the world was Martin Sheridan, a New York champion. He won a couple of Olympics with throws around 135 feet. But recently there has been astonishing improvement, especially in Europe, and an Italian champion has a record beyond 181 feet."

"What's the hammer-throw like, Mr. Cross?" Allan asked.

"Well! to call it a hammer doesn't seem appropriate," the veteran admitted. "When I first knew it, the hammer was an iron ball on the end of a rugged hickory stick about three feet six inches long. Later the iron or brass ball was connected to a steel wire with loops at the end for hand grips."

"Are Italians good hammer-throwers, too, grandpa?" Dave asked.

"Dave, I'm afraid that question will offend my good

10

Irish friend, Mr. Curry, for the great hammer-throwers have generally been Irishmen. Recently the Europeans have been doing very well, but through nearly half a century the world's best were huskies with names like Flanagan, McGrath, O'Rourke, Ryan and O'Callaghan."

"Are the Irish just as good at javelin throwing, grandpa?"

Mr. Cross smiled at his old chum. "No, son, I must admit that the Irish aren't very good at spear hurling, although it was an event in the Tailtean Games some centuries ago. But long before that, javelin throwing was a Greek pastime and it was one of the five events in that pentathlon I told you about. When the Greeks hurled it, the spear was only three feet long and was a war weapon as well as a sport tool."

"However, in the modern Olympics," the veteran continued, "the javelin has a steel point, on a wooden shaft and is about eight and one-half feet long. In 1936, a German athlete won the Olympic title but usually the champion comes from Finland or Sweden."

"What is the secret of javelin-throwing?" asked Allan, who had a very inquiring mind.

"Unlike hammer-throwing, Allan, strength is not as essential as speed, agility, and the ability to get a smooth flight. I once saw Matti Jarvinen, the Finnish champion, make a throw of 235 feet—and it was a grand sight to see that spear arc gracefully through the air. Certainly throwing a javelin has much more attraction than putting the shot.

"And yet, I liked shot-putting in my day," Mr. Cross added. "It has been quite a disappointment to me that during the past thirty or forty years Canada

11

has never produced a headliner in any weight event. Although Johnny Courtright did very well in the javelin and reached 217 feet. I can't explain the slump. But there's no doubt about it."

"That's quite true," Jack agreed. "There isn't a single chap in the whole country who can putt the shot as Harry Gill did back around 1910."

Mr. Cross listened carefully to his friend, then took a long, keen look at his thirteen-year-old grandson and remarked, "Dave, you have long arms, good weight and the lines of a champion. You could regain Canada's lost laurels. I know enough to coach you properly."

Running
a Mile

CHAPTER 3

While Dave was thinking about the suggestion, Mr. Curry quickly advised, "You're not my grandson, lad. But, I'd say, don't turn to weight-throwing."

"What's wrong with the weights?" Mr. Cross countered sharply.

"They're all back-breakers, Ed, and you know it," Jack retorted. "You practice, practice, practice. Most of the time you train alone because no one else wants to throw shots or hammers. Then when you are ready to go places, you find yourself competing in a faraway corner of the field, where you won't hit anybody and where nobody can see you. Who ever cheered a discus competitor?"

"I think your views are extreme, Jack," his old friend asserted. "If young Dave isn't the ideal build for, say, a shot-putter, then I don't know an athlete from a bale of hay."

"Oh! I think Dave has the body of a great miler," Jack contradicted. "Besides, there's no event like the one-mile run."

"What makes it so good, Mr. Curry?" Allan interrupted.

"Well! first of all, it's a challenge to a man," Mr. Curry declared. "For more than fifty years, runners have been talking about the four-minute mile. It seems to be the goal of all track athletes."

"I can remember my father telling me about W. G. George," Mr. Curry continued. "George was an English runner who competed in the 1880's. Even at that time, the mile was the big event at a track meet, and George happened to come along in a period when there was lots of competition."

"That reminds me, Jack," Mr. Cross broke in, "about the story I once heard of the first time young George raced against a more experienced runner named Cummings. This Cummings held back for a while and encouraged the youngster to set the pace. But every time that George's heels came up, Cummings tapped them with his fingers and forced the leader to change stride and lose confidence. Soon he dropped back and Cummings came on to win."

"That wasn't fair," Dave declared. "I'd rather George had won."

"You're quite right, lad," Mr. Curry agreed, "and eventually he did whip Cummings. In fact, George

14

became so good that he was the first man in all history to run a mile in a time better than 4 minutes and 13 seconds."

"Was that really fast, Mr. Curry?" Allan asked.

The veteran smiled. "It was just so fast, my boy, that even twenty-five years later it was still the world's record. Since then, of course, there have been some great milers and faster times."

"Tell us about them, Mr. Curry," Allan suggested, as he sprawled on the ground and cupped his chin on his hands. "I think mile running would be great. Don't you, Dave?"

"I'm not saying," his chum answered warily. "I'm just listening."

Jack turned to his veteran friend. "You and I, Ed, have seen some great milers in our years. Do you remember George Orton?"

"Oh! yes," Ed answered pleasantly. "I recall my father taking me to see Orton run one of his early races. He competed for Toronto Lacrosse Club and then he joined the New York Athletic Club. He was so good that he won the United States open mile championship six times. And he could also run cross-country and any distance up to ten miles. In fact, I would say that George Orton was the best middle-distance runner that Canada ever produced."

"But were his times as fast as those made by that English runner named George?" Allan inquired.

"No! they weren't, but there are reasons for that," Mr. Curry explained. "You see, some milers don't race to break records; they run to win. If their opposition is slow, their times are slow. But! give them com-

15

petitors who can force them to break a record or lose, and they push themselves to break that record."

"The best mile-runner I ever saw," continued Ed, "was Paavo Nurmi, who was generally called the Phantom Finn. He could really gallop. He was one of those fellows who didn't race against any competitors; he just ran against time. When the starting gun fired he pressed his own stop watch which he wore on his wrist. At the end of each lap he looked at his watch. If he was behind schedule, he speeded up; if he was ahead of his plan, he slackened. Nurmi seemed to be quite unemotional; it didn't appear to make much difference where his opponents were. He just ran to his own time-table. I think his best mile time was pretty close to 4 minutes and 10 seconds."

"Did he ever compete at the Olympics?" asked Allan.

"He certainly did and I saw him in the Games at Paris," Mr. Curry remembered. "He was first competing in the 1500 metres race."

"Metres," murmured Dave. "What are metres?"

Grandpa Cross quipped, "I'm better at figures than Jack, so I'll explain that. All European and Olympic distances are measured in metres rather than yards. Actually a metre is 39.37 inches, which is a little under one and one-tenth yards. So at the Olympics they don't run 100 yards, they run 100 metres or close to 110 yards. Neither do they run a mile for the nearest distance is 1500 metres, which is about 1640 yards."

"Now let's see, what was I recalling," continued Jack. "Oh! yes, about that 1500 metres race at the 1924 Olympics. As I recollect, it was run early on a

16

Thursday afternoon. The competitors were the world's best middle-distance runners, and right from the start that sturdy, smooth-striding Finn dashed to the front, ran like a clock, and won the race in time that was more than three seconds better than the previous Olympic record.

"And that wasn't all he did," Mr. Curry continued. "Just a couple of hours later he started in the 5000 metres race and his competitors were mostly fresh runners who were concentrating on that one distance. But again the great Finnish athlete not only won but also made a new record."

"Wasn't that the year he also won the 10,000 metres cross-country race, Jack?" cut in Mr. Cross.

"That's right, Ed. It was probably on the following Saturday. The day as I recall was terrifically hot. There were thirty-nine starters and most of them were 'knocked off' by the blistering heat and never did get back to the Stadium. But Nurmi finished fresh, more than a third of a mile ahead of the second placer and won his third Olympic gold medal in three days."

"Have Nurmi's records been beaten, Mr. Curry?" Allan asked.

"Yes, Allan, they have," admitted the old-timer. "It seems that records are only made to be broken. But I'd say, in my opinion at any rate, that Nurmi was the greatest middle-distance runner of all time. And he was a picture athlete—upright, strong, smooth, long-striding, unemotional, dependable. He had everything. Don't you agree with me, Ed?"

"Yes! I wouldn't quarrel with your opinion, Jack," Mr. Cross replied. "To me, one of his greatest assets

17

was his consistency. A friend of mine timed him over twenty-four separate laps in a long race, and there wasn't a variation of more than two seconds in any lap."

"How should a boy train for a mile race, Mr. Curry?" Allan questioned.

"How old are you now, son?" Mr. Curry countered.

"I'm thirteen, sir."

"Well! you're much too young yet for mile races," the veteran advised. "At your age, even a quarter-mile is rather long. Mile runners come late. Most of the good ones I've know were at their best about twenty-four or so. You see, a miler has to have strength and stamina, as well as being a great judge of pace."

"What do you mean by judge of pace, Mr. Curry?"

"I mean that a runner learns by experience whether he is running too fast or too slow, whether he should take the lead, also if he is reserving enough strength for a fast last lap.

"Glen Cunningham, for instance, was a miler who could judge pace perfectly," Mr. Curry explained. "Before one race he said to a track official, 'I'm not in very good shape today. Will a 4.20 mile win the race?' Upon being assured that it would, he ran and won and his time was just two-fifths of a second away from his promised speed.

"Yes," concluded Mr. Curry, with a sly look at his old friend Mr. Cross. "I'd certainly say that middle-distance running is far more interesting and fascinating to a young athlete than throwing spears and hammers and discuses all across somebody's nice green fields."

"I still think that Dave's frame is that of a typical weight-man," Mr. Cross affirmed stubbornly. "He

18

could be the man to bring back to Canada the glories of Knox and Gill and Gray."

"Sure he could," emphasized his equally determined friend. "But why make him break his back to break a record? Why couldn't he become the first man in the world to ever run a mile in four minutes. What's wrong with that, Ed?"

During the heated discussion, young Dave looked from one debater to the other and carefully weighed the argument. Allan was all for the mile but Dave made no comments. At last Grandfather Cross said, "Jack, let's leave it to the lad himself. Which would you rather be, son, a miler or a weight-thrower?"

Dave smiled, crawled slowly from the steps in case he had to get away quickly, then raised his head and decided, "Neither. I'd rather be a hockey player like my dad was."

Syl Apps
Talks to
Boys

CHAPTER 4

Dave Cross was a hockey enthusiast l right and the desire to play the world's fastest g e was quite natural, for his father had been a good layer prior to the World War, and Dave had grown up in that environment.

To Dave there was no off-season for hockey. Even in summer evenings, when other lads preferred   atch baseballs, he would go to the barn, reach for his old toothpick stick and a hard rubber ball. Then with real enjoyment he would go outside and shoot the ball against the wall of the barn until his wrists gradually strengthened like whipcord. Of course, the effect wasn't quite the same as actually shooting pucks into a net, although Dave's imagination enabled him to picture the most amazing goals. Some were backhanded, others were sizzled ankle-high; there were hard shots and soft shots and slap shots. Each was dependent upon his own mental conception.

But just so soon as the leaves changed colour and winds blew colder, Dave and Allan went straight from school and daily tested the rubbery ice. Just as soon as it would hold them, they gingerly stood close to the shore and slithered a puck to each other. Then one Saturday morning, after a cold night, the ice was thick enough for skating, and the season opened.

True, there were no bands to usher in that opening. There were no spectators to cheer the players or howl at the referee. There was no big clock to record the time. There were no lights to signal goals, or writers to extol the virtues of the participants. Instead, there were just a half-dozen boys, skating and stickhandling around a bend in the river, firing the puck between a couple of stones, and sometimes stopping play to search for the rubber, even fish a lad out from a hole in the ice.

To grown-ups, the play might have seemed crude, but that's where Canadian hockey begins; that's what gives it the start that produces finished players at an age when the youths in other countries are just beginning to skate. And Dave Cross was one of those tens of thousands of Canadian boys who started in that outdoor nursery.

During the summer months Dave thumbed the record books and studied the goals and assists and penalties. If you asked him how many goals Charlie Conacher scored in 1931, or when Turk Broda had first played with the Toronto Maple Leafs or the year that

21

Red Horner had 167 minutes in penalties, the correct answers would have popped out quicker than a cup of coffee in an automat. He could have earned 100 marks in any examination relating to the hockey career of Syl Apps.

Dave not only started to play hockey early but he read everything relating to the game. On Saturday nights he and Allan sat entranced as they listened to the hockey broadcast and pictured themselves in every play. During the hockey intermissions they matched their judgments with the experts.

Then something unusual happened. One Sunday Dave rushed home from Sunday School, dashed into the house and shouted, "Mom, do you know what?"

"No! What?" laughed his mother.

"Guess who's coming to town?"

"Let me think," his mother suggested with a smile. "It wouldn't be the Prime Minister of Canada. He's busy at Ottawa. It couldn't be the President of the United States. Could it possibly be a fellow named Syl Apps?"

"How did you guess, Mom?" the boy wondered.

"Well! I didn't exactly guess, Dave," his mother admitted, "for I have to bake some pies and help serve at the church social on Friday night. Did I hear you say you couldn't go because you expected to have too much homework?" his mother joked.

"Oh, no! you didn't," Dave answered promptly. "I'll come home right after school and do my work and get cleaned up. Besides," he added, "I couldn't think of your carrying those pies all that way."

That Friday was the longest day of the year. It

seemed that the hands on the school clock were so heavy that they couldn't run uphill. But! sharply on the stroke of the last bell, all the boys dashed from the rooms as though they had been crouching on a cinder track awaiting the crack of the starter's gun.

That afternoon, Dave reached home in time which made a new record for the course from school desk to cookie jar. With a zest for life he attended chores, finished studies and did such a thorough scouring job on himself that Grandpa Cross declared, "They better put numbers on all the boys tonight, and then issue programmes. If they don't, some of the parents won't be able to identify their own children."

Sharp at 6.30, the boys, and there must have been a hundred of them, started to eat. From the head table, Mr. Cross, who had been invited to introduce the guest, couldn't help but notice that the glances of the boys were like strings running directly from all the eyes and converging on one person, the guest of the evening.

Mr. Cross did very well. He said he had heard that a good introducer was a man who stood up to be seen, who spoke up to be heard and who shut up to be appreciated. He said that as he had to live in the town and wanted to be appreciated, he would speak very briefly. Then he quickly recalled Syl's achievements and concluded, "He's the kind of a man that every father would like his son to become."

When Syl Apps arose to speak, it seemed that every voice-box in the crowd was so crammed with sound that it was about to burst like an over-filled toy balloon. It was a welcome that the guest would long remember.

Syl thanked them for their greeting, then suggested

that if they had any questions, he would answer them first, before he began his talk.

"What player hits you the hardest?" was his first query.

Syl smiled. "A lot of them do that," he admitted. "Red Horner hits hard, but he is on my own team and I just meet 'Red' at practices. Eddie Shore can really sock. So can Chicago's Earl Seibert. But I would say that Bucko McDonald hits as hard as anyone; you really bounce from one of his body checks."

"Who is the best centre in the National Hockey League?" one lad asked. Then he blushingly added, "Other than yourself, I mean."

"I could honestly have answered that question, even if you had included myself," Syl answered with a grin. "The best centre player in professional hockey is Milt. Schmidt of Boston Bruins. He is a good skater and a smart stickhandler; he's also a great playmaker, has a hard shot and is strong right to the end of the game."

The boys asked more questions about the best goal-keeper; the fastest shot; how to learn to play; are right-hand shots better than left; was Morenz a great player. Before Syl could answer them all, he felt he should begin his real address.

He told them stories of funny incidents. One was about the lazy player who, during a practice, skated slyly to the rail and whispered to the trainer, "When the coach isn't looking, throw some water over me. Coach thinks I'm loafing and I want to appear as if I'm really perspiring."

Syl told them stories about the courage of hockey players. He recalled that one goalkeeper had been hit on the head with a flying puck and was so badly cut that eight stitches were required. There was no substitute goalkeeper available, so the injured player, after the sewing, had his head wound in a bandage that was as big as an Indian turban. Then he soon returned to the ice, played a great game and allowed only one goal in thirty minutes.

Then Mr. Apps told the boys about early hockey. The game started in military garrisons at Halifax, Montreal and Kingston. At one time skates were steel runners clamped to the soles of ordinary boots. Old magazines shoved inside stockings were the first shin-pads. Goalkeepers were not allowed to fall on the ice and had to remain upright. Goal-posts were just a couple of iron rods, without nets or a crossbar, and were frozen into the ice. Goal umpires, instead of being protected by heavy wire cages, had to stand on the ice and wave a flag when a goal scored. The puck could not be poked ahead to another player; instead it had to be passed on a line or backwards.

Finally, Mr. Apps spoke seriously and told them that life, too, was a game; that in life they must make sacrifices for the good of others; that they couldn't make a success alone and should give full credit to all those who helped them; if they broke the rules of life that they would be penalized.

Then Syl ended by repeating the Sportsman's Code to "keep the rules; keep your temper; keep yourself fit; keep faith with your comrades; keep a stout heart in defeat; keep your pride under in victory; keep a sound soul, a clean mind and a healthy body."

Dave Plays
Indoor
Hockey

CHAPTER 5

The address of Syl Apps made a great impression on
Dave. It taught him that games are more than just fun
and that they also make a boy stronger in body, mind
and character. But even more, at that particular time,
Dave became keener than ever to develop into a great
hockey player like his idol.

During that winter, Grandfather Cross found that
the farm work was a little too heavy for his years. So,
when young Dave passed his examinations and was
ready for high school, Mrs. Cross and grandfather
agreed it would be a good time to sell the farm and
move into town. Dave like the idea very much for it
would mean he would not have to take the long bus
ride twice a day. But what seemed even more important was the fact that the town had a new hockey arena.

"It will be great playing indoors," Dave told his grandfather.

"I'm not so sure that it's the best thing for a young lad," Mr. Cross replied.

"Why not?" asked Dave.

"I'm not a hockey coach, lad. I'm a track and field man," Mr. Cross admitted. "But! I have observed some things in the development of young athletes and I prefer outdoor to indoor training. It seems to me that when boys play hockey on rivers and ponds they develop legs and strengthen their lungs. Even shovelling snow from winter ice before you can even play is great for muscles and the wind."

"Yes!" Dave countered, "but it's not one-sided. Indoors you learn to play position and you get good coaching."

"That's true, son," the grandfather agreed. "But on ponds and rivers where a score of youngsters are on the ice at one time, a player has to stickhandle or he can't make headway. And they tell me that stickhandling is becoming a lost art in big hockey. Perhaps the boys are coming indoors too quickly," Mr. Cross added.

"But! Grandpa, don't forget I've turned fourteen years old," Dave explained. "I've been skating outdoors for eight years. Perhaps I'm ready for an arena and a team with a uniform. I'll see Mr. Ashley as soon as high school opens."

The town of Westport was very anxious to give its youth a chance to play in good surroundings. They believed that sports were a good thing for a community.

"Sports keep boys busy in their spare time," the mayor declared. "They teach them to lose without whining and to win without bragging; they encourage them to sacrifice themselves for the good of the team and to take directions from elders without complaining."

So the town built a very fine arena on ground that had been swampy and an eyesore to the neighbours. The arena had an ice surface almost as large as the area in Maple Leaf Gardens, and comfortably seated about three thousand spectators. It had all the big red circles, colourful blue lines and trimmings associated with the major rinks. Under the rows of blue-painted seats there were several clean dressing rooms and showers. It was a grand place for the boys and a splendid centre for the community.

But the town wasn't content to just build a rink; it also provided for Mr. Ashley a recreational director. It was one of his jobs to get boys interested in hockey, to form teams and leagues and to get young men to coach the boys.

Soon after he moved to Westport, Dave called on Mr. Ashley.

"My name, sir, is Dave Cross and I want to join a hockey team."

"That's fine, Dave, we can find a place for you. How old are you?"

"I'm fourteen, sir," Dave answered, as Mr. Ashley wrote down, "Midget section—big enough for juvenile."

"Do you happen to be a goal-keeper, Dave?" Mr. Ashley asked.

"Oh, no!" the lad chuckled. "I'm a centre player; shoot left hand."

Mr. Ashley smiled as he remarked, "Goal-keepers are getting scarce. Tell me, Dave, why don't boys want to play goal? Are they afraid they might get hurt?"

"No! I don't think that's the reason, Mr. Ashley. You see, when boys play outdoors on the ponds, the fellow that is pushed into goal is mostly the smallest or the one that isn't a good skater. Very few want to play that position because there isn't enough action in goal, and you can get very cold on river ice."

"Well! Dave, I can see you won't become a goal-keeper," Mr. Ashley agreed. "But we can find a team needing a good centre, so you look me up as soon as ice is in the arena."

Early in November, Dave attended a meeting to which all the young hockeyists had been invited. Mr. Ashley told the boys that they would be grouped according to ages into pee-wees, bantams, midgets and juveniles. Leagues would be formed and group winners declared. Then these group champions would play against winners from other areas until the best team in the whole province was found. Each team would have a good coach and would wear sweaters having the same design and colours as the teams in the National Hockey League. They would have numbers, too.

Right from the start Dave got the breaks. He was assigned to a team that wore Maple Leafs colours. He was a centre player, so he was given Syl Apps' number 7. Then at the second practice, he discovered that the coach had reason to be especially interested in him.

Before the boys took the ice, the coach explained that young teen-agers always kept themselves fit, so there wasn't much need for them spending time in

29

exercising or running outdoors. He had always felt that runners should train on cinder tracks, swimmers in pools and hockey players on ice. So the first fifteen minutes they could skate around without sticks, getting the feel of the ice. That would give the coach a chance to size-up their skating abilities. For another quarter-hour, he would let them skate while carrying sticks. Then, if they weren't too tired, he would drop a few pucks on the ice and let them play shinny for a few minutes.

That plan suited the boys perfectly. They whirled around the rink, circled the goals, staged little races of their own and had a barrel of fun. Then, with the sticks, they zigged and zagged through imaginary defences and made sensational attempts to score on the phantom goalie. When they were given pucks they slapped and banged the rubber in all directions and revived their memories of Saturday mornings on the ponds. But all were quite content to retire with the final whistle and to sit on the locker benches while they removed their boots and stroked their aching ankles.

The second practice was more advanced. The coach separated his goal-keepers, defencemen and for-wards. He looked them over carefully, paired the defenders and grouped the attackers into left wings, centres and right wings. Then he sent a goalie into the nets, dropped a defence in front of him, and started forward-lines in waves of three from the far end.

A midget line then skated down, it tried to pass the puck around the defence or split it apart, then shoot on goal. Still another and another line followed. The players had been instructed only to stickhandle or pass

30

the puck; there would not be any body-checking, boarding or slashing. "Too many players are injured in practice," the coach said.

Most of the playing seemed rather crude for many of the lads were strangers and the season was much too early to compare skills. However, the line of Allan Long, Dave Cross and Jack Boone seemed very smart and confident and had a finish to their attack that surprised coach "Buck" Blair.

Indeed Buck was so pleasingly startled by the performance of that line that as the boys were filing from the ice he stood at the gate and said to Dave, "Stay here a minute, son, I'd like to talk to you."

Dave stepped aside and the coach inquired, "Where did you learn to play hockey, Dave?"

"Just on the river," Dave replied. "Of course, my dad taught me a lot, too."

"Well! you look an awful lot in your appearance and style like a fellow who played with me on the Maroons," Buck told him.

Dave smiled as he asked, "Was that man's name Cross?"

"It sure was," the coach half-shouted. "How did you know?"

"That happens to be my name. He was my dad," Dave proudly answered.

"I might have known," Buck laughed. "You're going to be rangy like he was; and I hope you're just as smart. You looked nice there today. This team will go a long way."

Westport Wins
Midget Final

CHAPTER 6

All that first season, Dave's team, which had been nicknamed the Beavers because they had mostly learned hockey on the river, had been much too good for local opposition. In fact, they had been so successful that the coach had to give them a lecture about keeping humble.

Just as soon as it was evident that they would win their group, the coach cut a practice session in half and called the boys into the dressing room. When they were all seated, he stood at the end of the room, draped one leg over a chair and said,

"Boys, I want to tell you something about life. We are running a hockey team and we want to win every game we play; but your friends who give you this rink and make it possible for you to play are more interested in turning out good citizens than they are in developing champions.

"So far, you have won all your games; some of them by lop-sided scores. Most of you have taken the games in your stride; you have been good sports and have earned the respect of your opponents and fans.

"But!" he continued, "a few of you have become swell-headed. When you are given a stiff check you resent it. You threaten to 'get' your opponent and the next time he comes down you slash or jab or trip. Then when you are given a penalty, you jostle the referee, argue over his decision and try to make him look bad.

"Boys! that's not smart hockey. When you foolishly attack an opponent and are penalized, you hurt your team. They are forced to play five against six, and your mates not only don't score during those two or five minutes, but they also have to go all-out to prevent a goal against them.

"Even more important, you're hurting yourself. You're developing the idea that you're much too good for your opponents, that they have no right to interfere, that the rules of hockey were made for others but not for you. Boys! that's stupid. If you carry those habits into life you'll find yourselves lonesome and unpopular.

"I know that those who need that advice will accept it as coming, not so much from your coach, but from one who is old enough to be your father and is still your friend."

Then Buck told them they were already town-winners, but the toughest games were ahead. They would have to meet the western leaders and then, if victorious, would have to play the winners of the eastern sections for the provincial title.

In Buck's opinion, they were good enough to make the finals; and they did. They defeated the Huron Red Wings by 7 to 5 on neutral ice and were set to meet the Rideau Rangers at Maple Leaf Gardens in the finals.

There were bantam, midget and juvenile titles at stake on that late March Saturday morning, but the midget game attracted the most attention for both teams were considered to be the finest prospects in some years. The sportswriters had enthused about the Beavers and Rangers. Many professional clubs had sent their scouts to look over the young prospects, and the players on both Montreal Canadiens and Toronto Maple Leafs who were to play a Stanley Cup playoff in the evening, were sitting along the rails watching the lads who a few years later might be filling their own positions.

When the Beavers and the Rideaus came on the ice, the blue and red sections in the big arena were well-populated, and seated in a box directly behind the Beavers' bench were Dave's proud mother and his equally proud grandfather.

This was the first visit of Mrs. Cross to the Gardens and Grandfather Cross carefully explained about the markings on the ice; the lights behind the goal that flashed when a goal was scored or a period ended; the penalty clocks high up on the north wall that showed the number of the penalized player, the length of his sentence and the time remaining. Mr. Cross pointed aloft to the big sportimer that weighed four tons and had four large faces, each showing the elapsed time to an exact second. Then higher overhead were championship banners swaying gracefully, and finally on the far side, about sixty feet above the ice, was the radio gondola where Foster Hewitt aired the coast-to-coast hockey broadcasts.

As the two teams warmed-up before game time, the experts were pleasingly amazed at the appearance of the young teen-agers. The Beavers wore the Toronto uniforms of white jerseys with the big blue maple leaf on the front and the large number on the back, and blue pants; while the Rideau lads wore the Ranger outfits of Royal Blue jerseys with the name in big red letters across the front, with red pants and blue stockings.

But even more resembling the big leaguers than the uniforms were the pre-game habits of the midgets. The goal-keepers who weren't any higher than the top of the net carefully scraped the smooth goal crease with their sharp skates, then pushed the scrapings neatly behind the net. The youngsters lined-up at the blue lines, soberly received the puck from a defenceman and took their shot on goal; then skated around to loosen muscles that were really not old enough to have stiffened.

But beneath those outward indications of confidence, the lads were really suffering, and Dave was particularly conscious of his surroundings. He knew he was now playing in a rink where all his sports heroes had made their names famous. Syl Apps, Milt Schmidt, Howie Morenz, Marty Barry, Frankie Boucher, Nels Stewart had all skated up and down his centre lane.

Dave knew he would not be mistaken for them, but he did want to at least look as good as they did when they were only fourteen.

Then the referee blew his whistle, the puck was faced, the game was on; and the butterflies in Dave's stomach were quickly forgotten in the excitement of the play.

Both teams had been well coached. They knew the rules, skated well, stuck to their positions and didn't seem to tire. The defences stopped attackers with both body and sticks, and cleared the puck to the sides. The forwards stickhandled smartly, made neat flat passes, got in good scoring spots and even hid on the outer corner of goal creases awaiting shots they could deflect into the net.

But most of them had a weakness and a very important one it was—they were poor in shooting. In mid-ice and over the blue line they were all right, but close to the goal they couldn't get the puck off the ice; the shots were soft or they were wide of the net.

However, the first-line centre player on the Beavers didn't have that weakness. He whipped the puck low, hard and dead-on in the way that Babe Dye and Charlie Conacher must have fired them when they were fourteen. Furthermore that same lad could not only shoot hard but, when close-in, he could pick an opening not an inch wider than the puck itself.

Towards the end of the game when the score was tied and the Beavers' number seven circled the Rideau defence, faked to the left, then backhanded a sizzler into the Rangers' net, a man seated in front of Mr. Cross turned around and said, "Now I've seen everything.

36

That lad is a natural. He's doing things at fourteen that some pro's never learn to do. I'll have to talk to him."

"Better see me first," warned Mr. Cross.

"Why do I have to do that?" the scout inquired.

"I'm his guardian," answered the proud grandfather as he smiled at Mrs. Cross.

Fighting the High-School Bully

During his first and second years at high school, Dave was content to play hockey in the winter, and he advanced from the midgets to the juveniles. He was just as sensational with the fifteen-year-olds and scouts were watching him closely, eagerly awaiting his sixteenth birthday when they hoped to be the first to place him on what they called a negotiation list.

This race for the stars had become so keen that club managers had been known to telegraph the name of a prospect to the headquarters of the league just one second after midnight on the day when a boy reached his sixteenth birthday. Mr. Cross didn't like that. He felt there should be more consideration given to the desire of the boy and to the plans of the parents. So he

38

and Dave's mother guarded Dave's birthday very closely and warned the lad to also keep the secret.

At school, Dave was not a number-one boy, but he studied without fuss, plugged for examinations, and usually passed with a couple of C's, mostly B's and the occasional A.

In the Westport school, the High Y group was well organized. The members met once a week in private homes and planned dances and arranged for trips to industries or even to other cities for Easter vacations. They brought in athletes and other famous folks to address them. They were all fellows who were good students, outstanding athletes and had a keen interest in what was called school spirit. They were also, of course, believers in the "body, mind and spirit" purpose of all Y.M.C.A. members. Inclusion in the chapter was only by nomination and a vote, and it was considered a very high honour to be elected to the group.

Dave had been asked if he would permit his name to be voted upon and he readily agreed. But just as soon as "Beef" Smithers heard about it the trouble began. Smithers was about the biggest boy in the school and wherever he went he threw his weight around. He was one of those fellows who pick quarrels, talk loud and think that might is right and that a fight can settle anything. He was very envious about anyone who defied him and he was particularly jealous about Dave whose hockey fame was widely esteemed.

Nominations to High Y were supposedly secret so that a person who was rejected would not be publicly humbled. However, by the "grape-vine" route Beef had learned that Cross was up for election.

So, one day with no attempt to be subtle, Smithers approached Dave on the school steps before the students had gone into their classes. Instantly, he shouted, "They tell me you're trying to crash into High Y. Well! take a tip from your superiors, Cross, you'll never make it."

"Why not?" asked Dave.

"In the first place, it's for smart guys. In the second place, it's for students with school spirit, something you haven't got. You call yourself a hockey player and you play for the town Beavers and don't even practice with your high school team. Along comes a track meet, and where's the great Cross? He's away up there in the back row. I'll bet you don't even know the school yell. And as for fight, you couldn't lick your chops," he added defiantly.

Dave's face was a deep red. He knew there was some truth in what Smithers had said, for he hadn't played any game except hockey and he had played all his hockey for outside teams. But! he didn't like to be told that he was afraid, especially in the presence of so many chums.

Blazing indignantly, Dave retorted firmly, "I heard what you said about my poor school spirit; I can take that. But what makes you think I can't fight?"

"Well! I'll say it again, Cross," Smithers boomed in a tone that could be heard twenty-five yards away. "What's more, I say you're yellow, and if you want to do something about it, I'll meet you behind the stand at four o'clock."

Dave was cornered. He wasn't a trouble-maker. He didn't like scenes. He was one of those live-and-let-live lads. But this dare was more than he could take. Smithers was taller, heavier, and a year older, but this wasn't a time to reason things out. Instead, a thoroughly aroused lad promptly accepted the challenge and declared, "That's all right with me, Smithers; four o'clock."

The news of the fight spread like a forest fire in a drought. Small discussion groups formed all over the grounds. Hopes were definitely with Dave, for Smithers had been the school bully and he had left in his wake a long line of lads who were anxious to see him whipped. But they weren't sure that Dave was the one to do it. They admitted he was wiry, strong and fast. But could he punch? That was the big question.

During the afternoon Dave's mind was not closely on such subjects as English and History. Instead, he was considering the best way to whip his adversary. He seemed to have come to a very satisfactory conclusion for at least he didn't appear to be downcast over his prospects.

"What's your plan, chum?" asked Allan Long as the two walked over to the agreed location.

"He could be stronger than me," Dave admitted, "and he might wear me down if we fight very long. So I'm going to 'shoot the works' in my first punch," Dave confided to his buddy.

When the two of them reached the area under the stands, it seemed that half the students had already gathered to see what to them had become the real

41

Battle of the Century. As Dave approached, there was an excited cry of, "Here he comes," and the ring opened to let him through.

"Didn't think you'd come, kid," sneered Smithers. Dave attempted a smile but didn't bring it to full bloom.

There were no speeches, no time-wasting, no instructions, no referee. The spectators circled widely around the two fighters and someone teasingly shouted, "Go!"

Instantly Dave leaped at his opponent. He swung a hard right that caught the unprepared Smithers flush on the chin and followed with a sharp left close to the right eye. It rocked Beef and caused him to half fall.

"Sock him again, Dave," someone yelled. But Dave hadn't the killer instinct; he didn't like to hit anyone when he was down. He stepped back and, as he did, Smithers regained his feet and swung blindly and furiously. Dave side-stepped and Beef missed by a foot.

Suddenly, the circle of spectators broke and scattered as though a howitzer had found the range. The fans ran to all compass points, leaving only the two battlers. There was reason for their hurried escape.

Walking briskly, the principal appeared and commanded, "Stop that fighting instantly. Both of you report to me in my office tomorrow at ten minutes to nine. Smithers, you go north. Cross, you go south."

The next morning the two fugitives faced each other in the principal's office. "From what I hear, Smithers, you provoked this fight," the master began. "You have a reputation for doing that. How long yesterday's fight lasted I don't know. Certainly long enough for you to get that black eye," he added, with a show of satisfaction.

Then, turning to Cross, he said, "I'm rather surprised at you. You don't seem to be a boy who looks for trouble. But you definitely found it this time."

He continued, "Regardless of who is right or who is wrong, both of you made that fight possible. I must maintain discipline. I must punish those who break laws. For the next two weeks both of you are to report to the detention room at 3.30 each day. You can sit at opposite sides of the room if you so prefer," he concluded.

Smithers took his licking badly. "I didn't lose the fight," he told listeners. "Cross jumped me before I was ready to start. But I hear that the High Y has already withdrawn his name, so I was the winner any way you look at it."

The students, however, were quite sure they knew who had been the victor and they didn't hesitate to support Dave. Even the teachers, in hushed tones of course, had expressed pleasure that the school bully had been trounced.

Dave was content with the outcome of the fight itself. He felt he had struck "quickest with the most." But he wasn't completely satisfied with the turn of events, for he did feel that there was some truth in what Smithers had said about his lack of school spirit.

Fails in
Weight-
Throwing

CHAPTER 8

Through the winter Dave continued to play hockey with the Beavers and they had advanced from midgets to juveniles to juniors and were still the class of their division. He was just as brilliant as in his previous years. Every expert who looked at him agreed he could have a great career in professional hockey and the scouts were still scanning provincial records for his birthday, but Dave's grandfather and mother were giving them no help in their searches. They wanted the lad to have fun and get an education before he became a professional hockey player.

Meanwhile, Dave's conscience was bothering him. He felt he was letting his school down. He wasn't doing anything for it athletically, and the teachers and students rather resented that one so talented should fail to help them at school track and field meets. They needed the points he might earn for them.

One spring day his chum, Allan Long, recalled, "Dave! you remember that night when your grandfather and Mr. Curry were talking about champions and styles and the events that would suit us best?"

"Yes! I remember, Al," Dave replied. "Grandpa had said I had the build of a weight-thrower. He might have been right, you know. I wonder if he was."

"Well! Mr. Curry got me so interested in mile running that I hope to try it some day. I've already worked up from the quarter to the half; and you just wait, Dave. I'll make a good showing at the mile in a couple of seasons. Why don't you try the weights, just for the school title, and see how you get along?"

That idea appealed to Dave. He thought it over very carefully and then decided to turn out for the discus and the shot. But he concluded that he would do it "on his own." He wouldn't ask his grandfather for any advice, for anybody, so he thought, could compete in those two events and do well. Of course, after he had won them he would casually tell the folks at home about his success.

So, one afternoon, after school, Dave jogged over to the track. He handled the discus, hurled it casually, and walked away. Then he went to the putting circle, picked up the shot, found it wasn't too heavy and heaved it a couple of times. But he didn't stay around very long and he wasn't anxious to let it be known that he would compete in those events at the school competitions. It seemed to him that if he had shown real interest it would have proved that "Beef" Smithers had been right after all and that it was Smithers' criticism that had induced him to do something for the school. He certainly didn't want Smithers to get that credit. Besides, he was so sure that his natural strength would enable him to do well at any throwing competition.

However, when the list of entries was placed on the bulletin board on the day before the school meet, the name of Cross appeared, and comment buzzed through the corridors.

"Cross is going into the discus and the shot tomorrow," one student said to another. "He should have picked the soft events. Smithers has won those titles the last two years and he will murder Dave. What's more, he will enjoy it."

The games were held following school and most of the students had remained particularly to see the outcome of this duel, for they knew this could be a bitter battle so far as feelings were concerned.

"The next event on the programme," Coach Anderson announced over the loud speaker, "will be the 12-pound shot. Will all entrants come to the centre pit?"

Evers, Stinson, Johns all putted. Then Dave picked up the iron ball and stood in the ring. He raised the shot to his shoulder, took a couple of jumps and threw. The distance was fair but the coach declared, "Foul throw. No need to measure."

Dave looked up surprised and rather bewildered. "Foul," he muttered. "What was wrong with it?" The coach beckoned to him and quitely informed Dave that a shot could not be thrown like a ball. Instead, the rules required that it be pushed from the shoulder. Dave nodded.

On his next turn, Dave was quite conscious of his arm position. He wasn't going to make that mistake again. But he was so keen to get the shot away perfectly that he failed to notice that as the ball left his fingers, his right foot had hopped over the whitewashed circle. Again Mr. Anderson was compelled to announce, "Foul! No need to measure."

Meanwhile, the experienced Smithers had putted clean and far. His form had been faultless, his distances were good and he was leading the field.

Soon it was announced, "Cross—last putt." Dave's confidence was oozing. He was wishing he hadn't been so self-assured and had asked his grandfather for some coaching. However, he hadn't and he just had to do the best he could.

He picked up the shot, held it well up in his fingers, recalled that he had to putt it legally, remembered that he must stay inside the circle; then hopped, reversed and putted. It was a fair toss but Dave had lacked co-ordination; each act was stiff, and reduced his power. Naturally, Smithers won the event easily and Cross was fifth in an entry of seven.

Later in the afternoon the discus throwing began. Smithers handled the implement expertly and hurled it far down the field for a new school record. Dave, in his three attempts, was so clumsy that the discus wobbled in the air and landed on its edge instead of on the flat.

After Dave's last miserable attempt, "Beef" strutted over to Dave and jibed, "So your grandfather was a champion weight-thrower! He sure must have been proud of you today. I could throw farther with my left than you could with your right."

Dave could take defeat gracefully. He had played enough games to know that you couldn't win them all and that sport teaches you take the bitter with the sweet. He knew he had been foolish to think he could do well against experts without coaching or training.

But! that criticism of his grandfather really hurt. Dave was a family boy. He was loyal to his mother and his grandfather. Even as a young lad he was readily aroused when anyone teased him about his dad. But that ridicule from Smithers had impressed Dave that he had let his grandfather down, that he had permitted the old champion's reputation to be sullied. That wasn't good. That couldn't be repeated.

Decides to Try Pole-Vaulting

CHAPTER 9

When Dave returned home after that distressing performance at the school meet, he talked with his mother.

"I'm not much good in athletics," he deplored. "I'll have to stick with hockey."

"Grandpa's big interest, Dave, is running, jumping, throwing," Mrs. Cross explained. "He was so good in those events and he was disappointed when your dad took to hockey. He had hoped that someday a Cross would again be a track champion. He kind of counted on you, Dave. Perhaps you would do better if you tried again and asked his help."

Dave's enthusiasm for tracks and pits had been so dampened that he didn't feel he could ever try them

49

again. However, he admired his grandfather and didn't want to hurt him. So when Mr. Cross intimated he would like to see the High-School district track finals at the big university stadium, Dave suggested that the two of them go together.

From their seats high-up in the stands, away from the roaring student crowd, the veteran keenly watched each event, discussed the competition and talked about the varying styles.

"They do things quite differently from my day, Dave," Mr. Cross recalled as the sprinters were getting ready for 100 yards dash. "When I began, the tracks were often dirt tracks at Fair Grounds and they were hard as concrete. In fact, I even ran some races on macadam roads in the main streets of a town.

"We didn't have starting blocks, either. Some of the sprinters took stand-up starts instead of the crouch which came along later. But the boys made good times. My friend, Walter Knox, was timed 100 yards in nine and two-fifth seconds. There were four watches on him, so there was no doubt about it."

"Was that time good, grandpa?" Dave asked.

"It was so good that only two other Canadians, Percy Williams and Cyril Coaffee ever equalled it. I'd say that after all the improvement in cinder tracks and shoes and coaching during the past thirty or forty years that there isn't anyone in Canada today that could touch Knox's time."

"What do tracks do to improve times, grandpa?" Dave asked.

"Some tracks, because of their good drainage and spring, are known as fast tracks," Mr. Cross explained.

"Every country has a couple of them where it is easier to break records."

"Did you ever run on grass, grandpa?"

"No! I never did, although they do in Australia. I had the idea that a grass course would be slippery and rather slow. But I must be wrong, for Australians are good sprinters and the times they make are quite fast."

"Where was the best track you knew, grandpa?"

"Well! Dave, I've seen some good ones," Mr. Cross recalled. "White City in London was good. Some of the American universities were splendid. But I'd say the best of all was the one constructed for the Olympic Games at Berlin in 1936. The top was made from brick dust and Jesse Owens, the great coloured runner, told me it suited him perfectly."

"Who was the best sprinter you ever saw, grandpa?" Dave asked during a lull in the races.

"It would be a toss-up between Owens and Percy Williams. Percy was a Vancouver high school boy when I first saw him. He competed in Toronto in 1927 for the Canadian championships. He was seventeen or so at the time. Not tall, but quite sturdy, and had a good pair of legs—not too heavily muscled.

"The day I watched him he competed in both sprints but didn't get into either of the finals. I felt rather sorry for the lad for he had travelled all the way from the Pacific Coast and was forced to return without even getting honourable mention. In the East he was soon forgotten.

"But! the following spring," Mr. Cross continued, "I read in the paper that a Percy Williams, running on grass in Vancouver, had been timed 100 yards in 9.7

seconds, and that he would have done better had he not slipped. I doubted the timing and so did most of my friends.

"However, those doubts were soon removed for Percy again came East for the Canadian Olympic Trials. This time the sprints were run in those metrical distances I told you about, and the Vancouver boy was sensational. He won the 100 metres race in faster time than Hahn, Walker, Craig, Paddock and Abrahams had won the previous Olympic championships. Then he had a short rest, started in the 200 metres race, won his heat, qualified in the semi-final, and then cleaned-up the field in the final."

"How did he do at the Olympics, grandpa?" Dave asked eagerly.

"He made the name of Canada famous in every country where men laced on spiked shoes," Mr. Cross enthused. "Remember, when Williams went to Amsterdam he was still a teen-ager and he was running against the fastest, cagiest sprinters in the world. Everyone of them was a national champion. Even to get on the mark against such competition was a tribute to one's ability, and there were over eighty starters from thirty-seven countries entered in the 100 metres.

"After a series of heats and semi-finals, there were only six finalists remaining. They were Wykoff and Macallister from the United States; London from Great Britain; Lammers, Germany; Legg, South Africa and, of course, our Canadian Percy Williams.

"When the starter barked the 'Get Ready,' the stands were stilled; it was one of those tense moments that crowd into sports. At that instant, the strain on the competitors is severe. I have felt it often. You want to get away flying but you know you mustn't beat the gun. But every runner knows you can win a race at the start as well as at the finish.

"On that day, as I recall," Mr. Cross continued, "Legg broke ahead of the gun; then Wykoff offended. Those two false starts might well have shaken a young runner, but Williams had nerves of steel, and held on both breaks. Then, on the third start, the runners got set, the gun cracked and the six sprinters dashed down the cinders. The Canadian was the first to show in front; he hung on to his narrow margin, gradually inched farther ahead and won going away. It was a brilliant victory."

"What happened in the 200 metres race, grandpa?"

"Let's watch this mile race first, Dave. I'll tell you about that later if we have time. Do you know anybody in the mile, son?"

"Sure do, grandpa," was the answer. "My pal Allan Long is the third from the inside. He's got a good chance. He has run a 4.32 mile."

"That's very good for a young lad," the veteran agreed. "He can build-up nicely on that during the next few years. There's the gun!"

"What do you think of the runners, grandpa? Do you like Allan's style?"

"They're a nice bunch of athletes," Mr. Cross asserted. "Allan has good form for a miler. Easy stride, about long enough for his height; but he kicks his heels a little too high. His arm action is easy and not pronounced."

"Should Allan win, grandpa?"

53

"Unless a person knows the runners well, you can only guess," Mr. Cross experted. "I would say he should place all right, but whether or not he could win depends on his judgment of pace and his reserve strength. They are things within, not without."

Now they were coming down the far stretch and entering the last curve on the final lap. Allan had been running in third place, but just as he reached the bend he stepped out from behind the second runner and passed him. Then, still on the curve, he challenged the leader.

"That's bad," exclaimed Mr. Cross.

"What is, grandpa?" Dave exclaimed. "Is it Allan?"

"Yes. He shouldn't try to pass on a curve. He's running yards farther than the man on the inside. He should have made his drive on the far stretch or waited for the last fifty yards straightaway. There! he isn't catching the leader. The fight exhausted him. He's slipping."

The second man caught Allan. He finished third.

"That's too bad," Dave groaned, "but I can see that a race can be lost in the head as well as in the feet. Allan must have gone five yards farther on the curve, yet he was only three yards behind the winner."

Through the afternoon Mr. Cross and Dave chatted freely, and closely watched the scores of Westport High. All the time, the veteran was trying to find some enthusiasm on the part of his grandson for a special event. Dave liked the hurdles and sprints and was keenly interested in the mile because his chum was in it. The weight events seemed to bore him. The running broad jump, the high jump and the hop-step failed to arouse any enthusiasm. The only event remaining, other than the relays, was the pole vault.

"There's a nice event, Dave," his grandfather commented. "It's a good combination of running and jumping. Requires strong arms, co-ordination and sure is spectacular."

"Did you like it, grandpa?"

"Yes! I did, Dave. It seems to me that for a real thrill I preferred it to all others."

"What made you like it, grandpa?" Dave asked.

"Well! you train for months for a sprint and it's over in a few seconds," his grandfather explained. "Even a mile has come and gone in less than five minutes. Weights have a lot of work to them. But! in pole-vaulting, I've seen fellows competing for two or three hours before a winner was declared. Besides, it's great fun to shoot up into the air, then drop twelve feet into a soft pit. Syl Apps was a pole-vaulter, you know, before he made any name in hockey," Mr. Cross added casually.

"What's that?" Dave almost shrieked. "Apps a pole-vaulter?"

"That's right," Mr. Cross responded while trying to control his own enthusiasm. "That's right, and a good one, too. He won the Canadian championship."

"He did?" shouted an incredulous Dave. "I wouldn't have believe it. Never knew it. It must be a good event all right."

Learning
From the
Ground Up

CHAPTER 10

That chance remark about Syl Apps, who was Dave's favourite athlete, had been a spark to ignite a desire in the boy. If pole-vaulting was exciting enough for Syl, it should be good for him, too, Dave reasoned.

At the evening meal on the day following the district track meet, Dave said to his grandfather, "I've been doing some thinking, grandpa. Could I become good enough in a year to compete at the games we saw yesterday?"

"Good enough!" chuckled the veteran as he glanced at Mrs. Cross. "Good enough. That's not the half of it. You could win it—providing you were properly coached."

"I had in mind that you might do that, grandfather."

The two of them agreed that even a year wasn't too long to catch up with fellows in other schools who had been vaulting for several seasons. So they decided to start training right away. They quietly arranged with the high school coach to borrow a set of jumping standards and a pole and asked him to treat the whole affair confidentially.

"That's all right with me, Mr. Cross," Coach Anderson declared. "My father used to tell me about you and I'll be very pleased for any coaching help you can give us. If you want to work behind the scenes, that's all right with me."

When looking around for a place to train, Mr. Cross said to Dave's mother, "You know, Mary, we have lots of room on this property. We even have a driveway but still have to get a car or build a garage. I've been thinking that we could construct a narrow runway at the side of the house, dig a landing pit in the backyard, put in a box for the pole and do our jumping right here."

"Do you think Dave would develop more right at home than he would at a track?" Mrs. Cross inquired.

"You really need both places, Mary," Mr. Cross agreed. "But I have always had a notion that what we used to call proximity had a lot to do with an athlete's ability."

"Proximity. That's a new word to me," laughed Mrs. Cross. "Don't tell me you can also coach languages, dear. What do you mean by proximity?"

"I mean that a boy who lives close to playgrounds has a better chance to succeed than one who lives some

57

miles away," Mr. Cross explained. "A lad whose home is next door to a skating rink is going to learn to skate at an early age and he is going to be playing some hockey every day there is ice. A boy whose backyard faces a golf course is going to be swinging clubs and whacking balls long before his cousin is going to know the difference between a fairway and a bunker. That's why they get baseball players in United States, hockey players in Canada and skiers in Norway," Mr. Cross added.

"That means, dear," Mrs. Cross broke in, "that if we have a vaulting runway, or whatever you call it, right at home that Dave will come along quicker and better than if he had to go two or three miles to practice?"

"That's right," grandfather concurred. "He will be a natural. You wait and see. He wants to be a vaulter, and an athlete always does better in a sport he likes."

So Dave and his grandfather levelled and rolled the ground, put in the slide box for the pole, dug a nice soft landing pit and began training for the long road to a championship. How far that road would lead neither of them knew at that time.

Before they really got started, the veteran athlete said to his pupil, "Dave, before we start jumping, I want to tell you something about vaulting. It's an old sport, probably started by shepherds in ancient times who would use their strong crook to enable them to jump across streams. In fact, at one time, there was pole-vaulting for distance as well as height.

58

"Just when pole-vaulting became a modern sport, I couldn't say for sure. But! I do know that in my father's day, that would be around 1880, pole-vaulting was a regular event at the United States championships and a fellow named Baxter could clear eleven feet.

"Now when I started vaulting, Dave, the pole was made of solid wood with a long spike in the end to jab into the hard ground. Some times that pole broke. I remember that Ed Archibald, who competed for Canada at the Olympic Games in Athens in 1906, had that misfortune and he barely escaped the jagged end stuck in the ground as he dropped from the bar."

"But this pole isn't hardwood, grandpa," Dave broke in.

"No! Dave, it's bamboo. It whips better, has a longer life and isn't so heavy to carry. Besides, there is now a box into which the pole slides and that has made it possible to do away with the long steel point. Indeed, they are now trying aluminum poles and I hear they are great."

"Now tell me what I have to do with this pole, grandpa," Dave asked eagerly.

"Well! first of all, son, get the feel of the pole. Place your right hand here with the palm up; now grip the pole about here with your left hand with the knuckle side on top.

"Feels awkward, doesn't it, Dave? You'll get used to it. Don't grip the pole too tightly. That makes you tense. Now run a few steps with it. That's all right."

"Now let me have the pole, son, and I'll show you how to angle it while you're running with it. You see, if I hold the pole to one side or the other it will tend to throw me off balance or make me run sideways. If I hold the pole pointing upwards, it will throw my body backwards instead of forwards and will also take more effort to bring it down into the slide. See what I mean, Dave?"

"Yes sir."

"Now, here's the correct style, son. Hold the pole parallel with the ground or even angling slightly downward, with the point of the pole leading straight to the take-off slide. Like this, Dave." Mr. Cross said as he held the pole properly and jogged a few yards.

"When do I start jumping, coach?" asked the impatient pupil.

"Not tonight, Dave," counselled grandfather. "Just practice that grip until it becomes natural. Then get that angle of the pole down pat. We'll make haste slowly but we'll get there."

The next practice Dave took a lesson in jabbing the pole into the wooden slide.

"The jab, Dave, should be strong and accurate. As the pole is about to hit the slide box, the top hand grips firmly and the lower hand slides upward until they almost touch. I'll show you roughly and then you practice awhile."

Then Dave tried grips and pole-carrying, and attempted several easy jabs. On later nights he learned how to gauge the height of the hands on the pole, and how far to run before taking-off.

Through several training sessions, Dave never took even one vault. Finally, becoming almost desperate, he asked rather bluntly, "Grandpa, don't I ever get off the ground?"

"Next week, Dave, we will begin jumping. I know how you feel, my boy," Mr. Cross explained with some sympathy. "Training is not as much fun as performing. I haven't wanted to be hard on you, but pole-vaulting is one event that requires good form. A vaulter with ability plus style will leap a lot higher than a fellow who just jumps without learning all the details. It's easier to count from one to ten if you know all the numbers in between," he added.

Then one evening, the coach said to his pupil, "Dave, you're getting along all right. Tonight, you can take a couple of jumps. Now remember, get the right grip, carry your pole slightly down, jab the point into the box firmly, slide your lower hand upwards, and climb with the pole. When your legs are over the bar, turn your body towards it, push the pole away, then drop to the pit. We will learn what to do with your arms and legs later; but just now take a couple of jumps and get the feel of it."

Dave tried to remember all he had been told. Then he ran, jabbed, climbed, kicked vigorously, cleared the bar with his body but knocked it off with his arm.

"A good try," the veteran declared. "How did it feel?"

"I felt good until I got into the air, then I didn't know what to do," Dave declared. "I guess we didn't get that far in our training."

"That's right, Dave," Mr. Cross explained. "Your take-off was quite good. The rest of the style will come along just as well."

Through the summer, the practices were getting

more interesting and results were improving; but when Dave got up to nine feet, progress seemed to stall.

"That appears to be as high as I'll ever get," Dave said in a discouraging tone. "That is about my limit."

"Tut, tut, son!" Cross Senior reproved. "You've been doing all right. I can see what you require. The first need is more speed on the runway. We'll get to the track early next spring and do some sprinting."

"Sprinting?" asked the surprised boy. "What has that to do with pole-vaulting?"

"Most athletes would ask that question, Dave," his mentor explained. "But running is the foundation of any game. If you haven't legs, you can't stand up, and if you can't stand, you can't play. This is especially true in jumps. Every vaulter should also be a good sprinter. An aeroplane must have speed, you know, before it takes off."

Ridiculed
by Smithers

CHAPTER 11

During the following winter, which was Dave's final year at high school, he played with both his high school team and the Beaver juniors. His hockey talent was still the talk of the town.

During one of the junior finals, a sportswriter in one of the city evening papers related, "Last night, Dave Cross, Beavers' centre, scored five goals—each of them in a different way. He fired a long, high one from the blue line that was so fast that Andrews heard it pass but didn't see it; the second was a slap shot that scorched the ice; the third was scored on a smart play when Cross circled the defence, crossed in front, faked a shot, saw Andrews sprawl, then lifted the puck over the prostrate netkeeper; the fourth was a backhander that

63

sizzled; and for his last goal, the young Beaver sensation stood on the edge of the goal crease and sharply deflected Long's pass directly into the net. In appearance and in result, this Cross is the nearest approach to Apps who was about the same age when he was starring for Hamilton Tigers."

Dave naturally read everything that the newspapers wrote about him. He was a level-headed lad, not given to conceit, but that comparison with Apps pleased him, for he was determined to follow Syl's trail.

His arch enemy "Beef" Smithers also goaded him to succeed in pole-vaulting, but he didn't do so intentionally. Smithers had joined the Westport Beaver juniors and was compelled to centre the third line on a team where Dave was the superman.

The success of Dave irritated Smithers, and whenever possible "Beef" made needling remarks. In the dressing room after one game, Smithers sat in the opposite corner and shouted so that everyone could hear, "Well! Cross, you may be a fair hockey player, but you sure were the world's worst weight-thrower. You were never much help to your school at a track meet. By the way, wasn't your grandfather a shot-putter or something?"

"Yes! he was," Dave hollered back, "and what's more, he was also the best pole-vaulter in Canada."

"That's a laugh, Cross," Beef retorted. "You weren't any credit to the old boy in the discus or shot. Why don't you try pole-vaulting and give us another chance to chuckle?"

Dave had learned not to pop-off publicly. He had been told that empty vessels make the most noise and he believed it. So he attempted a smile and replied, "Perhaps I will try pole-vaulting, Smithers. Perhaps I will."

Ridicule discourages some young athletes but it really spurred Dave to try even harder. He was determined to not only make Smithers twinge, but even more he was keen to do justice to his family reputation. He wasn't going to allow his grandfather's record to be attacked by Smithers or anyone else.

However, that year the hockey season dragged on until late March and it was early April before frost was out of the air and there was enough warmth in the ground to permit outdoor work on the school track. By now, his home runway had become too cramped for Dave; he needed more length, as well as the competition of schoolmates.

One day, Mr. Cross said to Dave, "Well! son, you've had some rest after your hockey. Are you ready to dig-in for your pole-vaulting?"

"Yes sir, I'm raring to go," Dave answered. "But about that sprinting, grandpa; do you really think I have to do that? Couldn't I just go and vault?"

"I'd like to say, 'Sure! go ahead'," Mr. Cross explained. "But I would be doing you a great injustice. A man has to save today if he wants to have money in the bank tomorrow. Similarly, a young athlete has to sacrifice in the beginning if he wants to become a top-notcher.

"Sure!" he continued. "You could vault right away; but you just be patient, my boy, if you want to be a champion pole-vaulter. You have to get more power on the runway."

"How will sprinting do that, grandfather?"

"Sprinting," the veteran explained, "not only increases speed, but it also develops a uniform stride. There's not much use measuring-off your starting point on the runway, if you find that some strides are short and some long. When that happens, you lose step as you near the slide box and you hesitate just at the moment you should be thinking of your jab and climb. That's not good. It throws you off completely. Every vaulter should be a good sprinter."

"Do you want to come to the track with me, or had I better go alone?" Dave asked.

"Dave, you would probably be upset if I interfered when other boys were present," Mr. Cross thought. "They might think you were being molly-coddled. I'll go to the track when you are vaulting and see what you are doing—from a distance, of course."

"But how will I go about sprinting? Will I do the 100 yards and the 220? Will you tell Mr. Anderson what you have in mind?" Dave asked.

"Yes! Dave, I'll do that. Your school coach is a very fine teacher. I'll work closely with him. My suggestion will be that you just practice starts, and then dash about fifty yards at your best. You will be surprised how your speed and striding will improve."

Mr. Anderson respected the veteran's judgment and was anticipating Dave's pole-vaulting success almost as much as were Dave and his grandfather. Each day, after school, Dave changed into his sweat-suit and spikes, got on his mark and sprinted down the cinders.

One day Smithers crossed from the infield, came over to the track, looked down on Dave and snickered.

66

"Well! well! Cross," he blurted. "First you were going to be a shot-putter; then you thought you might be a pole-vaulter. Now, before the season begins, you decide to be a sprinter. What's the big idea? Why don't you make up your mind?"

Dave looked straight down the track and replied without bitterness, "Don't worry about me, Beef, I know where I'm going."

Style First—
Performance
Later

CHAPTER 12

After a couple of weeks conditioning, Dave remarked to his grandfather, "That sprinting is great stuff. I'm not only running faster but my strides are more uniform. I took a few dashes on the runway and Allan counted the same number of paces each time. How about me doing some jumping now?" Dave asked.

"If Mr. Anderson agrees, I would think the time is ripe, son," Mr. Cross replied.

The school coach consented readily, so Dave began with the crossbar at eight feet, raised it to eight feet six inches and cleared it; got over nine feet all right, but stuck at nine feet six inches. That seemed to be his limit and Dave was again becoming discouraged.

"You better come and see me tomorrow, grandpa. I've reached my limit and the games are only a month away."

"Make it Saturday morning, Dave," Mr. Cross suggested. "Then we can have the track to ourselves."

The next Saturday, the two were early at the school grounds. Dave jogged around to loosen muscles, then went to the vaulting pit.

"What do you want me to do, grandpa?" Dave asked.

"We will put the bar at eight feet six inches, then raise it to nine feet," the veteran coach decided. "I'll take a look and see what you need."

Dave cleared the lower height easily, but just skimmed over the higher one. Then he stopped and inquired, "What's wrong, sir?"

"Dave, your ground work is splendid. There's nothing there that I would change," Mr. Cross affirmed. "But! in the air, you aren't putting enough energy into pushing away from the pole, nor are you kicking your legs out straight enough as you cross the bar. Now try that nine feet jump again and keep your arms closer to the body until you give that last instant thrust from the pole; then extend them to the full with a real push."

Dave was one of those young athletes who take instructions readily. So, he nodded his head, remembered to push away the pole and kick higher. He ran down, jabbed, climbed and cleared the bar by about six inches.

As he picked himself out from the pit, he looked up smilingly at his mentor and remarked, "Guess we're improving, eh?"

69

Mr. Cross agreed that the jump was better, but thought he detected another error. "Dave," he said, "let's raise the bar to nine feet six inches. You've never cleared that high yet. Just go through the motions yourself. There's something I want to be sure about before I make a suggestion."

Again Dave, now much more confident, measured the height for his hands, went to his starting mark, balanced the pole, ran, jabbed, soared but ticked the bar with his left foot and knocked it to the ground.

Naturally he was disappointed, "There you are, grandpa. That's the height that stumps me. Now try to solve that one," he proposed.

"All right, son, I will. What's more I think I can. I'm certainly not discouraged," he smilingly announced. "Let's put the bar up again at nine feet six inches."

They did, and Mr. Cross stepped back. "Now, Dave, get your pole. Now measure the height for your hands on the pole."

Dave did. Mr. Cross watched closely, then instructed Dave. "Now, raise both your hands six inches higher on the pole. That's right. Keep them there. Now go back and jump. Remember that kick and push. You can do this, son."

Dave was tiring, but resolved to make this a supreme effort. Once more he came hustling down that narrow cinder path. Then the pole slid into the box, the pole was straightening; his legs kicked as his arms straightened. He was up and over, and into the pit. Almost before he hit dirt he was looking up to see if the crossbar was still in position. It was, and he felt the satisfaction of a man who has just made a great discovery.

"That did it, grandpa," he shouted. "I can see it; my hands were too low on the pole. Gee! you sure are a great coach."

"I'm only helping, Dave," Mr. Cross observed. "You're the one who has to do the jumping. But, remember, while nine feet six inches is good, you still have to go much higher."

Gradually Dave upped his height. He had climbed one range. He was now challenging loftier peaks; and they were very formidable. However, he won the school title at ten feet six inches. That was a good vault but still quite a bit short of eleven feet three inches which was the district record. And the games were only a week away.

Dave Has
Pre-Meet
Jitters

How to improve by nine inches in a week was a haunting fear to Dave, and everything that happened during those few days seemed to make him more jittery.

All through Park Tech school the coming track championships were constantly in every mind and on every tongue. The athletes were weighing their chances, discussing whom they would have to beat, what times they must make, how far or how high they must jump. The students were keen to end the reign of Southern High who had dominated the meet for some years. Even the teachers and the principal were concerned about what would happen to school morale if old Park did not make a good showing. That tense feeling was carried like germs from non-competitors to the athletes themselves.

Then, to add to this feverish excitement, the school decided to have a pep night a couple of evenings before the games. At this event the school assembled on the stadium infield, practiced cheers, sang songs and listened to inspiring talks from principal and coach.

"This must be our year," the principal said. "For nearly ten years we have trailed badly. We always thought we had good material. The boys were smart in practice, but when they got into the stiffest competition of all they slipped. When they came to their final examination in athletics they just weren't good enough; they were beaten by fellows from other schools who didn't have nearly as much ability.

"But," he concluded, "those memories must now be forgotten. This year, we have the coach, we have the team, we have the school spirit; nothing can beat us. Do you agree?"

There was a resounding "YES" that must have been heard by the pupils away up in Mars High.

"All right," concluded the principal. "Park Tech expects that every man will do his duty."

To many listeners those words and all that enthusiasm had a helpful effect, but to Dave it rather lowered his confidence. He felt that he was the centre upon which school failure or success revolved. He continued to wonder how he could ever add nine inches to his best jump in one afternoon—and even then he might not win.

His grandfather noticed this lack of confidence but did not say anything to Dave about it until the day before the games. Then, during the evening the veteran remarked to Dave, "Well! son, you're looking rather forlorn. What's the trouble?"

"Grandpa, I'm discouraged," Dave admitted. "The meet is on tomorrow. We need to win the pole-vault badly and I'm the school hope."

"That's all right, Dave. What's wrong with that?" Mr. Cross asked.

"Just this," Dave replied. "It's as simple as two and two making four. My best jump has been ten feet six inches. Three other competitors have gone that high. How can I whip them all? It's asking too much from me."

"Let me tell you a few things, son," Mr. Cross answered. "I've been through a hundred of those pre-game agonies and I know just how you feel. I never competed in a single meet of any importance that I didn't have the jitters before the day or before the event. But! Dave, don't worry about that. It's the sure sign that you're a thoroughbred. A fellow that has no imagination never gets anywhere in sport.

"The thing to do, Dave," the veteran advised, "is to turn your imagination around and make it work for you."

"How do you mean, grandpa?" Dave asked.

"Just this. Right now you have a picture in your mind. You see yourself tomorrow in your event. In your mind, you get over nine feet easily; you clear nine feet six inches; you tick-off the bar at ten feet on your first try, but make it on your second. They raise the bar another six inches. You are now picturing that bar at ten feet six and you're saying to yourself, 'that's my limit; perhaps I won't even go that high.' But you do scramble over it, and then you are stuck. You can't go one inch higher. But three others can; and they do,

74

and they get the points for their schools. Then you are beaten, your school has lost, and you are an outcast. Now doesn't that describe your thoughts pretty well?" Mr. Cross concluded.

"Yes, it sure does, grandpa," Dave admitted. "But how can I get rid of that feeling?"

"Like I said, son," Mr. Cross explained. "Turn your imagination inside out. Instead of saying to yourself, 'I can't do it, I'm beaten, I'm disgraced,' just picture yourself coming-up to ten feet six inches and clearing it nicely, then going up three inches and three inches and three inches more. Each time your competitors are dropping out but you, in your mental picture of course, are climbing until you alone remain. Then you are the champion, your school has won and you are the hero of the meet. That's the attitude to get, son. It's called the positive one. It's the one that gives you hope and heart and courage. Remember! turn your imagination around until the sunny side is on top.

"Here's another thought, Dave. Am I boring you? Am I talking too much?" the veteran asked.

"No indeed, sir," Dave replied emphatically. "I'm feeling better already."

"Fine," grandpa chuckled. "Remember this, too. Your vaulting style is sound. Style in sport is like a foundation under a house. If it's sound, you can continue to build on it. Your form is your foundation. It's very good. It will carry you a foot higher than you have ever gone without any trouble."

"So remember, Dave," Mr. Cross concluded. "Think victory, not defeat. Use your mind to help your body."

"All right, grandpa, your advice makes me feel

much better. But how about tomorrow? What should I do on the day itself?" Dave asked.

"First of all, son, get to bed early tonight," the veteran advised. "Forget everything about the meet if you can. If you can't, be sure to picture only your success. Tomorrow, eat your usual breakfast and go through your normal morning. At noon, eat early.

"Food varies with athletes," Mr. Cross explained. "I used to like a small steak with baked potato, a couple of slices of toast and a baked apple. Some fellows prefer to eat very lightly before a meet, but I always did better if there was enough food to keep my stomach working. Of course, it also depends on your event; a sprinter doesn't need as much as a weight-thrower; while a vaulter may be competing for half an afternoon. So eat well, but avoid rich foods or excessive liquids."

"Also I preferred to get to the stadium early," Mr. Cross continued. "I found that I felt better when on the scene and in the company of other athletes than I did sitting at home thinking about what might happen. So I always got to the stadium early, dressed leisurely, jogged a little on the track; then returned to the dressing room and relaxed on a bench or table until my event was called."

"So that's the pre-game advice of an old-timer, Dave," Mr. Cross laughed. "Perhaps modern coaches have some new-fangled ideas. But those notions were pretty good in my day, and we got some very fine results from them. But! even if you forget some of my other advice, be sure to remember to say to yourself, 'I can win.'"

76

Call Me
Champ

CHAPTER 14

When Dave got to the big University stadium, the stands were rapidly filling with laughing, shouting, colour-waving students. Each school had its own section. Cheer leaders were prancing and coaxing and pleading for volume and harmony. Soon bands marched on and assembled in midfield. The athletes paraded around the track. Then, while everyone, competitors, officials and spectators, stood in respectful silence, heads bared, the combined bands played "The National Anthem."

The meet began with hurdles races; followed by sprints, and a couple of weight events; then the quarter and the half. Allan Long was first in the mile and Smithers had won the shot-put and was second in the discus for the orange and blue. Conditions were ideal and records were tumbling. At one time Park Tech had quite a margin in points for the school championship, but Southern High had always been strong in the jumps.

Dave had watched some of the earlier events. He had been keenly interested in the mile, and had cheered Allan Long as he stayed close to the leader all through the final lap, then jumped ahead in the last fifty yards, just as Mr. Cross had advised, and won by two strides.

As Dave praised Allan, the winner remarked, "Tell your grandfather that I did as he told me. I didn't pass on the curve."

Following the mile run, Dave noted that he still had about twenty minutes before his event began, so he left the track, went into the dressing room, found an unoccupied table in the far corner, and laid down for a little rest.

Soon, "Beef" Smithers, fresh from his weight-throwing victory, swaggered into the dressing-room and started talking to a group of athletes from various schools.

"How are you doing?" one athlete asked.

"Not bad and not good," Smithers replied.

"Why the double-talk," shouted another. "Are you winning or not?"

"Right now," Smithers said, "we're tied with Southern High. It looks like a toss-up between us. The pole-vault could be the deciding event."

"Who have you in that event, Smithers?" a chap from Eastview asked.

"Only a guy named Cross," he lamented. "Never

went over ten feet six inches. They have Blackstone. He won last year at ten feet eleven and a half, and they tell me he is much better this year."

"That's too bad, Beef," a listener sympathized. "Why didn't your coach bring along someone else?"

"Can't understand it," Smithers explained. "It seems that this guy's grandfather has some influence. Thought he could make a pole-vaulter out of his grand-son. It's too bad that Park Tech has to suffer just because an old man's reputation has to be kept alive."

At that moment, Dave, who had heard every word, rolled from the table and walked across to the group. Smithers noticed him coming, and stammered, "Oh! heigh! champ. Didn't notice you having a nap."

A year ago, Dave would have lost his temper and started swinging; but in the meantime he had learned to control himself. So he grinned as he retorted, "Thanks, Beef. When I win the pole-vault, just remember that you were the first to call me champ." Then he strolled out, crossed the track, and went over to the pole-vaulting runway.

At that moment the crowd was paying no attention to him, for the senior quarter-mile starters were on their marks. As the starter's gun fired, the runners swept forward in a small wave, for there were too many of them to run in lanes. So the competitors on the outside of the track were running faster to enable them to get a lead and cut-in closer to the pole.

It was all a pretty scene when viewed from the ground. The infield was a bright green and contrasted strongly with the dark cinder-track. The sloping stands were crowded with cheering students. The quarter-milers, in their orange, red, white, green, yellow or black jerseys, altered their colourful formations with each change in position. The runners were now rounding the last bend, the leaders were in the stretch, a red-shirted athlete was breaking the finish tape, with an orange-jerseyed challenger just a foot behind.

"That was a tough one for us to lose," Dave thought. "That gives Southern a lead again. It's definitely up to me to get that back. I'll do it."

Now the pole-vault officials had arrived with their papers. The cross-bar was being raised. The entries were being checked. Dave removed his sweat-suit and jogged up and down the runway. Then he paced himself carefully back to the starting point that suited him best and placed his sweat shirt on the ground beside that spot.

"All right boys," the chief official announced. "We're ready. Let's begin. Anderson, you're first," he shouted.

"How high is the cross-bar?" Anderson asked.

"You are starting at nine feet," the official replied.

Cross Breaks
High School
Record

CHAPTER 15

The pole-vaulting was under way and thousands of pairs of eyes were directed to the scene at the south end of the field.

Anderson, Swanson, Jonas, Kingdon, Carter, Torrance, Myers, Blackstone and Currie all jumped and cleared. Cross had drawn to vault last but informed the judges that he would not jump in that first round; he would wait for the next.

"Why don't you take your turn, Cross?" a competitor asked.

"The rules of vaulting permit me to start at any height above the minimum. I can clear nine feet all right, so I'm reserving my strength in case there should be a long duel at a greater height," Dave explained.

"Wish I had known that," the other lad declared. "It could be a help. It pays to read the rules."

The bar was then raised to nine feet six inches. Jonas, Carter and Myers failed in their tries. Cross took his turn and cleared easily.

The bar went up another six inches and Swanson, Kingdon, Torrance and Currie missed in their three attempts. The bar went up a few more notches.

Over the loud speakers the announcer informed the crowd, "There are still three competitors left in the pole-vault—Anderson, Humbervale; Blackwell, Southern High and Cross, Park Tech. The height is now ten feet six inches."

The spectators were keenly interested in this most spectacular of all events. Over in the Park section there was a general hope that their lad would win, but Smithers had invited some bitterness when he shouted to the girl cheer-leaders, "Better get your hankies out, girls; this is where Cross falls down."

Mildred Graham, Dave's companion at the school dances, blushingly resented Beef's remark. "You haven't much school spirit if you talk like that," she retorted. "Besides, you're not even right. Dave is going to win this event."

"Now don't tell me that our pretty cheer-leader is carrying that guy's torch," Smithers sneered.

But Mildred was right. Dave did clear that ten feet six inches, and so did Anderson and Blackstone. This was the best vaulting that the high school officials had ever seen and the announcer predicted the possibility of a new record as he declared, "I have two announcements to make. First, the team score is

Southern High 98 points; Park Tech 97 points; Humber-vale 95 points. Also, each of those three schools are still represented in the pole-vault. The bar is now at eleven feet."

Naturally, the crowd was keyed to fever pitch. The feeling was so intense that the usually noisy yelling had subsided and the throng was stilled. Anderson jumped and knocked off the bar with his leg. Blackstone cleared but his pole fell towards the crosspiece and dislodged it. Dave jumped, soared and wriggled over rather shakily. Anderson missed on his next two tries and was out. Blackstone asked to have the standards moved about three inches closer to the pit; then he jumped and made it.

Again came the voice from the loud speaker, "Ladies and gentlemen, the bar is now at eleven feet three and one-half inches. If Blackstone or Cross clear at this height, it will be a new record; the best in forty-five years' competition."

Blackstone jumped and missed. Cross vaulted and knocked it off for the first time. Again Blackstone tried; again he just ticked the bar. Dave followed with his second attempt, cleared it all right but unfortunately, while dropping, tipped the bar with his right arm. It swayed on the uprights, then toppled into the pit.

The third and last try was coming. Blackstone, a good vaulter and a sporting competitor, shouted to Dave, "Do or die, Cross."

"Best of luck, Blackie," Dave replied as cheerily as possible.

Blackstone ran, jumped, and seemed high enough. His supporters cheered as he was in the air, but their

83

shouts ended sharply, for Blackstone's arched chest just ticked the wood and it came tumbling down.

It was Dave's third attempt. He looked up at the restored bar. "Eleven feet three and one-half inches," he thought. He was just about to say to himself, "That's too high for me," when he remembered his grandfather's coaching and his mind recorded, "I can do it, I can do it."

He picked up his pole, again measured for his hand grips and returned to his starting position on the runway, about forty yards from the standards. Thousands of eyes were on him but he paid little attention to them. However, directly in his own line of vision as he glanced towards the crossbar, Dave noticed a man standing. The man waved his hat. It was his grandfather. Dave smiled and partially waved back. Then the veteran vigorously motioned to Dave's jersey which was loose and flapping and signalled for him to fold it in. Dave nodded and carefully tucked it.

Then, quite relaxed, Dave flexed his arms, gripped his pole, crouched slightly, ran, jabbed his bamboo pole into the box, and was whirled into the air. His body reversed, his legs kicked up and over, he pushed the pole away strongly, his curved body shot over the bar and his tight jersey just grazed it as he descended. But the bar stayed on as Dave dropped to the soft pit—a winner, a record-holder and the hero of Park Tech.

The next day, at school assembly, the principal said to Dave, "All the boys did well. But you, Cross, deserve special mention, for you not only won but you made good at a most critical time. We give you the utmost credit for a fine performance."

When the students clamoured for a speech from the record-holder, Dave hesitated, then rose and said, "I didn't intend to say this, but I should. I want to pay tribute to my grandfather who was one of Canada's greatest athletes. My margin of victory was so slim that if he had not signalled to me to tuck in my shirt, I would likely have knocked off the bar, just as Dick Blackstone did. Anyway, sir, thanks for your kind words."

Empire Games or Professional Hockey

CHAPTER 16

Dave's triumph in the high school championships attracted the attention of not only students but also experts in track and in other sports. One of those shrewd sport observers was Conn Smythe, general manager of Toronto Maple Leafs hockey team.

When the pole-vault ended, Mr. Smythe said to his chief scout, who was in the stand with him, "That Cross sure has a fighting heart. He also has the legs and the will-to-win that would make a great competitor in any sport. Can he skate?"

"He not only can skate, but he's the best-looking prospect in this part of Canada," the scout replied. "The only trouble is that he won't talk with us. He always says, 'See my grandfather.'"

"Well! why don't you?" Mr. Smythe inquired.

"We try, but the old boy is pretty cagey," the scout admitted. "He will listen, but he seems to have something else in the back of his mind. It isn't hockey and it isn't money. It could be pole-vaulting."

There were still other persons interested in Dave, and they came all the way from the United States' colleges. During the summer, there were no less than eight American and two Canadian schools interested in giving scholarships to the young student. These offers were not all alike but generally the visitors agreed to provide Dave with free education, including his books and special teaching, also they would find an easy job that would pay well and which would require work that would not interfere with his studies or athletics. In return, they would expect that Dave would attend classes, play on the university hockey team, join the track squad; and also pass his examinations. Most of them frankly admitted that they were attracted to Dave by his athletic talent, but they also sincerely desired him to be a good student, who would graduate honourably.

One of the strongest arguments used by the Americans was that Dave would not get good coaching or keen competition in Canada and that his athletic talent might be wasted in his native land.

Dave and Mr. Cross listened to the university scouts and thanked them for their interest. But the lad was only seventeen; he had just completed high school; he was contented and happy with his friends, and Dave's mother thought he could get a better education right at home. Besides, he was quite proud of his present athletic coach. So Dave enrolled at the University of Toronto.

Just as soon as he became familiar with his courses, his time-tables and the lecturers, Dave kept in condition at the track until there was ice in the arena. He started skating on the first night and was soon engaging in practice games.

Then, just as Dave was becoming interested in the schedule of the senior team, he was shocked by the advice that he would have to play with the juniors.

"Why is that?" Dave asked.

He was told that eastern Canadian universities were discouraging scholarships to athletes and that they had a rule that no freshman could play on a first team. But Dave had enrolled solely for education, and his hockey skill was so pronounced, that it wasn't fair, either to himself or his opponents, for him to play hockey with juniors.

The university sport directors agreed with Dave's viewpoint and explained it to the other universities. But they refused to make any exception to their rule, and Dave was advised that he could play with only juniors in his first year.

Meanwhile, Conn Symthe had heard about Dave's plight and he talked over the problem with the lad and Mr. Cross.

"This boy, they tell me, has great natural hockey ability," Mr. Smythe told Mr. Cross. "He's just at a critical stage in his development; but he should step-up in his competition, not down. No one learns to count to ten if they stay in kindergarten."

"What this young fellow needs, Mr. Cross, is a

season with Marlboro Seniors. That class would probably be beyond him at the start, but didn't somebody say that it's only by reaching beyond our grasp that we touch the stars?"

"But what about his studies, Mr. Smythe?" Cross Senior asked. "Dave doesn't want to become what they call a hockey bum."

"I appreciate your desires. I'm a university graduate myself," Mr. Smythe replied. "I agree that Dave wouldn't find much time for study if he took road trips. Suppose we decide that Dave will play only the home games. In that way he will get enough hockey, in tough competition, and will still be able to get his year."

All that winter, during his first university term, Dave, only seventeen, played senior hockey; but he wasn't competing against youngsters who were his own age and weight. Instead, he was playing with veterans who were tough, hardened and smart. In junior hockey he might make mistakes but no one would notice them; but if he made the same error in a senior game, the entire opposing team would quickly make a monkey out of him.

In senior ranks, Dave learned to stick to his position. If he didn't, an opposing centre would come driving through the spot he had vacated.

Another thing Dave had to be taught was to keep his head up when he went in on a defence. If he failed, he would be knocked off balance by someone he didn't know was even near to him.

He had to practice face-offs constantly. He had to know when to knock the other centre's stick out of position and when to let the opponent slap the puck.

He had to learn flip passes, flat passes and even fake passes.

Above all, Dave had to improve his shooting. With juniors, he had great luck but the seniors, at first, were too smart for him. He soon learned to look-up at the goal before shooting and to know that accuracy is more important than a hard shot that is wide of the net.

While Dave had a lot to learn he was an apt pupil. Indeed, by February, he was so smart that his play was the talk of the sporting world. In fact, he was doing so well that a scout for a major professional team offered him a contract at $7,000 a year if he would drop university and play with his club immediately.

The scout had approached Dave directly, and the boy promptly relayed the information to his grandfather.

"That's a lot of money," Dave believed.

"It certainly is, son," Mr. Cross agreed. "But my advice would be, 'Don't do it.' You've just turned eighteen. If you become a professional hockey player right now you won't have an educational background to carry you when your hockey ends.

"You're young yet, Dave," his grandfather counselled. "Why not have some fun. In August next, the British Empire Games are being held in London, England. If you could only make the Canadian team, you could have a fine trip to the British Isles and enjoy a wonderful holiday. This chance comes only once to an athlete. Professional hockey can wait. They'll see you later, my boy."

Dave's
Amateurism
Is Questioned

CHAPTER 17

The hope that he might be good enough, at eighteen, to compete for Canada in the British Empire Games had inspired Dave to train hard all through the early spring, through May and June, right up to the eve of the trials.

"You're out of the minor leagues now, Dave," his friend Allan had remarked one day.

"What do you mean, Al?" he asked.

"Well! you're through jumping against juniors in your own city," Allan explained. "You're now up against seniors, not only those from this territory, but fellows from right across Canada. You'll have to be the best in the whole Dominion—right from Vancouver to Halifax. Perhaps even from Victoria to St. John's,

Newfoundland. By the way, Dave, have you seen the standard set by the Games Committee?" Al asked.

"No! I haven't. Anything bad about it?" Dave inquired.

"Just this. You'll know whether it's bad or not," Allan informed him. "It came out in this morning's paper."

"Go ahead, Al. Break it quickly but gently," Dave requested.

"Well! the standards seem too high to me. They say that no pole-vaulter will be taken on the Empire team unless he clears twelve feet at the trials, and even then they are going to include only the winner."

"Say! that is kind of tough, isn't it?" Dave thought aloud. "Twelve feet and my best in competition has been eleven feet three inches. I have to improve nine inches, and even then I might not make it."

When Dave passed on this information to his grandfather, the veteran was not disturbed at all. "That's all right, son. I thought it might have been higher," he admitted. "But! let me tell you again, Dave. Your style is good; you can build height on it without much trouble."

"What should I do to get that extra nine inches, grandpa?"

"Success in pole-vaulting depends greatly upon the strength of your arms and upper body," Mr. Cross declared. "As you get older that power will come gradually. In the meantime, it will probably help you to go to the gymnasium when you can and do some rope-climbing. In my competitive days, most of the better vaulters were Y.M.C.A. members who were also good gymnasts. Get more strength in your arms and you'll get twelve feet easily. Outside construction work this summer would help," he added.

So for two months Dave worked outdoors in the daytime, and spent most of his evenings vaulting or rope-climbing. At times it was a rather monotonous life, but Dave was so keen to make the team and to see London that he didn't mind the extra effort.

So, on the day of the British Empire Trials, which also included the Canadian championships, Dave was sound in body and confident in his mind. Just how high he would vault he didn't know, for Mr. Cross was not a coach who asked his athlete to break records during training. "Keep your best jumps for the competition, Dave," he freely advised. "That's when they really count."

That morning and afternoon the best runners, jumpers and weight-throwers in the land had gathered in Hamilton. All had come with hope and desire. Each pictured himself on the deck of that ocean liner steaming out from Montreal for Southampton. Most of the dreams, of course, could not come true for the team was not a big one.

The weather had not been ideal for the games and along about the time for the pole-vault to begin, a drizzle started.

"This rain won't help," Dave remarked to Allan who had been competing in the mile run and was in the dressing room.

"It sure won't, Dave. And what's more, did you know that Smithers is entered in the pole-vault?" Allan asked.

93

"Smithers," echoed a surprised athlete. "What's he doing in the pole-vault?"

"I saw him on the track just now," Allan said. "He told me that his shot-put and discus marks wouldn't get him on the team, but he thought pole-vaulting was the easiest way to get a trip overseas. So he has been training real hard. I don't know what he can do, Dave, but he seems very cocky."

When the vaulting began, Dave's mind was not exactly at ease. The entry of Smithers had surprised him and the falling rain had discouraged him about beating the standard. However, those doubts and fears soon vanished when the competition began.

As the rules required, the vaulting started at ten feet six inches. The bar went up to eleven feet, to eleven feet six inches; and still there were five of the original nine remaining.

While Dave was clearing the eleven feet six inches bar, his friend Allan was standing near the track. As Dave went up and over, an official turned to Allan and said, "That fellow Cross isn't so smart."

"What do you mean, he isn't so smart?" Allan replied with some resentment.

"Those legs of his are worth $100,000. At least he could make that in professional hockey in ten years," the official explained. "Then he goes vaulting on a day like this with a slippery pole and a wet take-off. If he should break a leg, it might spoil his hockey forever. I wouldn't take those chances."

But there were some who would and Dave was one of them, for he jumped as fearlessly as though conditions were ideal. The bar was raised to twelve feet. This was the standard set by the Games Committee. Anyone who cleared that mark and continued to win would make the Empire Team, so all the remaining competitors were edgy at this try. To most of them, it would demand a supreme effort and, as they looked at the small strip of wood away up in the air, their faces were drawn.

Some of the vaulters were tiring, and they showed it; but Dave cleared on his first jump. Smithers surprisingly repeated on his second attempt. Three others failed in their three trials, and were out. Only Cross and Smithers remained.

The officials went into a huddle to decide whether they would raise the bar three inches or six inches. They favoured the higher mark and so informed the two competitors.

"That's not fair," Smithers complained. "Twelve feet three inches is high enough in this rain."

"It could rain in London, too," an official answered. "It might be well to know what you can do in bad weather."

Then "Beef" went over to Dave who accepted the decision without any question, and remarked slyly, "I guess they never heard you need your legs to make a living at hockey. If I were you, I wouldn't risk thousands of dollars just for a gold medal. Besides, you never jumped twelve feet six inches on the best day in your life."

Dave thought of some nasty things he could say, but that moment was one when he had to keep himself relaxed. He knew that Smithers was only trying to get him angry, so he laughingly replied, "Well! I'll send you a card from London anyway, Beef."

The officials, working under umbrellas, were now ready. The rain was increasing but the event had to be completed. So, Smithers jumped and missed. Cross tried, but his hands slipped on the taped pole and he never did get up in the air. Smithers again failed. Cross dried his hands on his jersey, gripped the pole tightly, ran, jabbed, climbed, kicked, pushed and cleared by a couple of inches. Smithers tried for the third time and once more kicked-off the bar. As competitors, officials and spectators ran for cover under the stands, it was evident that Dave Cross was Canada's champion pole-vaulter and a candidate for the British Empire title.

In the dressing room, someone said to Smithers, "Tough luck, Beef, you nearly made it."

"Don't be too sure I won't," Beef replied with a wry smile. "I have reason to believe that Cross won't be named to the Team. The games are for amateurs only, you know."

Just then an official opened a door at the end of the room and shouted, "Is Smithers here? Will he come into this room at once?"

When Smithers entered, the British Empire Games' President said to Beef, "I understand you have pro-tested Cross."

"That's right," he answered, "I have."

"What's your evidence against him," the officer asked.

"The British Empire Games are for amateurs, I understand," Smithers began. "Well! Cross isn't an amateur. He is being paid money by Maple Leaf Gardens for his services as a hockey player with Marlboro Seniors. I also understand that his grandfather received $1,000 for his consent and that Cross will play professional hockey with the Leafs next year."

The committee agreed that the information was important, that the charges were serious and that a decision should be made promptly.

"I've heard that charge before," a member admitted. "Perhaps if there's so much smoke there should also be some fire. Let's bring Cross in right now."

As Dave was entering, "Beef" attempted to leave, but the chairman said, "No! No! Smithers, you accused Cross. You stay here and make your charge in front of him."

Smithers didn't like that but he was cornered and again declared, "Cross played hockey for Marlboros and was paid for his services. Also, his grandfather agreed to have Cross play with Toronto Maple Leafs and was paid $1,000 for his help."

"Are those charges correct, Dave?" the chairman asked. "Before you answer, I should warn you that, if they are correct, you cannot become the Canadian champion and certainly cannot be a member of the Empire Team. In that event, Smithers would likely take your place."

Dave was not only angry with Smithers for making such charges, but he was also disturbed by the suggestion that his grandfather had been paid to secure Dave's consent.

"What do you say, Dave?" the chairman prodded. "Are Smithers' charges true or false?"

97

"I can only say that I have never personally received a cent for playing hockey," Dave answered crisply.

Smithers interrupted with a sneer, "Perhaps his grandfather got it all."

Dave, quite irritated, exclaimed, "Gentlemen, my grandfather never cheated in his whole life. You all heard about him. He held many Canadian track championships. He's waiting for me now; let us bring him in. I tell you, I'm an amateur. My grandfather can confirm it. I'll get him."

The committee waited until Dave and his grandfather arrived. "Good-day, Mr. Cross," the President greeted. "Take a chair. We must be brief as we have a lot of business to transact yet. I'll tell you our situation briefly."

He continued, "Smithers here finished second in the pole-vault. He has protested that Cross is a professional hockey player and that money has been paid to either Dave or to yourself for his services. We hope the charges are incorrect but we have to investigate them. Are they false?"

"Gentlemen," Mr. Cross began, "am I answering rumours or is there any evidence presented by Smithers?"

"What evidence have you Smithers?" the chairman asked.

"I haven't any written evidence, if that's what you mean," Smithers blurted. "But everybody knows the Marlboros were paid."

Mr. Cross turned to "Beef" and said, "Smithers,

98

you played three games with Marlboros early last season. Were you paid?"

"No! I wasn't," he answered. "I'm an amateur."

"So you see, gentlemen," Mr. Cross smiled, "on the evidence of Smithers himself, a player can play for Marlboros and be an amateur. But! apart from that, I can assure you completely that Dave has never been paid money for his sport services. He even went to a Canadian university instead of accepting scholarships from American colleges that would have involved money. As for myself receiving $1,000 for a promise to deliver my grandson to a professional hockey team, that, gentlemen, is a lie. True, I have been offered money for such a purpose, but I refused it very forcibly. What's more, if this committee wishes to draw an affidavit relating to Dave's amateur standing, I will solemnly swear to all the evidence I have now given you."

The chairman looked around at his committee members. Each nodded his head. "Thanks, Mr. Cross, and you, too, Dave. We appreciate your information and we believe you."

Then turning to Smithers, he said, "Perhaps we shouldn't have listened to your gossip in the first place. You have produced no evidence to support your rumours. Your protest has failed."

Wins Empire
Pole-Vault
at London

CHAPTER 18

Towards the end of July, the British Empire team from Canada assembled on the *Duchess of Bedford* in Montreal harbour. They were a youthful army of men and women. Most were runners, jumpers or throwers; but there were also swimmers, boxers, wrestlers, weight-lifters, rowers, fencers and cyclists. They were young, keen, strong, each with that eager alert air of a champion.

On the voyage, the athletes attempted to do some training but it wasn't easy. They could jog around the deck, but the rolling of the ship threw runners off-balance and the slippery surface invited some bad falls. The tank was too short for the swimmers, and the gymnasium wasn't much larger than a boxing ring.

100

While all the athletes were having some difficulty in their training, the boxers had the biggest problems to solve. The boxing trials had been held in Montreal just on the eve of sailing. All the competitors had been trained "to the bone" to make the weight required for their class. Naturally, when they won their titles and got on the boat, they were light and dry.

But! the ocean breezes made them hungry; and when they went to the dining room and read the menu, they found it included all the rich, tempting foods that they had been denied on land. Some of the boxers with very strong wills resisted the temptation and ate sparingly and wisely. When they weighed-in each day they found that their weights were uniform and they were still eligible for their fighting divisions.

But two or three boxers, particularly bantams and flyweights, had become so hungry that they couldn't resist the lure of fats and creams. The results were that their weights so increased that they literally "Ate themselves out of their classes." Indeed, despite the pleadings of their manager, they so gorged that when they landed they were far too heavy for their divisions.

The *Duchess*, after a nice trip, steamed past the Isle of Wight and into Southampton harbour on a bright clear morning. After disembarking and clearing customs, they all boarded the train awaiting to hustle them to London.

Dave had been sharing his berth on the boat with Nev Rich, a high-jumper from Saskatoon; and the two had become close friends. As they got on the train they were slightly confused. In Canada they had entered their train-car from the ends and had gone down the

101

usual long straight aisle with seats for two at each side. But in England, they entered small compartments through doors on the side, while the aisle was along the far side beyond the compartments.

Despite the strangeness of the train, Dave and Nev and their companions were thrilled with the fast journey, through small towns with names they had learned in history; past lovely English gardens, brilliant with blooming flowers; on into the suburbs of the world's largest city, and finally arriving at the big station. At last they were in the Heart of the Empire, and they were thrilled.

Quickly, they motored to their hotel in London's west end and were assigned to their rooms without much confusion. From their window, Dave and Nev could look across Marble Arch and Hyde Park Corner and into the beautiful park stretching for some distance along a traffic-crowded highway.

During the next two or three days, those athletes who didn't have to drastically cut down their weights, were taken on London tours to Westminster Abbey, St. Paul's Cathedral, the Tower, the Houses of Parliament, Buckingham Palace and the usual round of tourist spots. They walked along Piccadilly Circus, the Strand, the Embankment and the roads they had so often read about. They signed their names at Canada House where they enjoyed tea and biscuits, and were entertained at country homes. Then, having regained their land-legs, all social activities instantly ceased.

"From now on," the manager of the track team told his charges, "you will be under strict rules for eating, sleeping and training. We will, from here in, concentrate on the purpose for which we came. There will be a session at 10 o'clock tomorrow morning at White City Stadium, and another one in the afternoon at 2.30."

The next morning, at 9.30, the athletes left the hotel, walked to the subway and got in the train that whizzed them to an underground station, near to the Stadium.

The big field amazed the athletes. The infield was so smooth and green that it had the appearance of a mammoth bowling green. The track was wide, smooth and springy. The stands were rather far from the track but they encircled the field and streamed up so high that there was seating space for 90,000 spectators.

Soon the thrill of participating in such a vast enclosure was surpassed by the concentration in their training. The sprinters practiced starts; the middle and distance runners jogged methodically around the track; the throwers and jumpers heaved and leaped. There was such a massing of activity that the entire stadium had the appearance of a huge track meet all being conducted at the same instant.

The practice hour passed quickly, and the Canadians retired while the Australians took their turn. The Aussies were strong in sprinters and hurdlers; great in high-jumpers, broad-jumpers and hop-steppers, fair in weight events but up till now had not been exceptional in pole-vaulting.

But Dave, from the stand, took a keen interest in their vaulter. Critically, he watched the style of his Aussie opponent and checked the height of his performance.

"What do you think, Dave?" Nev asked the expert.

Dave smiled. "You're the fellow that has to worry

about the Australians," he replied cheerily. "They sure can high-jump; must learn that from the kangaroos. Personally, Nev, I expect my battle will be with a chap from South Africa. They tell me he can do thirteen feet any day in the week."

Dave didn't have that rumour confirmed until the fourth day of the games.

The pole-vault was to begin at 2.30 and the broadcast of the event was to be radioed around the world. Again, as on his previous big days, Dave had pre-game jitters; and not without some cause. He had won the Canadian championships at twelve feet six inches; but the Empire record was thirteen feet two inches. He was already in the dressing-room, feeling a little sorry for himself, when a messenger entered and inquired, "Cross in this room?"

Dave answered, signed a receipt and was given a telegram which he hurriedly opened. It was a message from his grandfather and mother and it read, "Remember, a Cross always does better in combat. Keep fighting."

With that inspiration on his mind, Dave left the dressing-room and crossed the track to the vaulting zone.

There were nine entries for the pole-vaulting—two from England; two from South Africa; one each Australia, New Zealand, Jamaica, Northern Ireland and Canada.

The vaulting began at ten feet six inches and worked up in six-inch rises until twelve feet six inches, and even then there were still four competitors remaining. At that height one missed, until at thirteen feet an Aus-

104

tralian and a South African were still battling with
Cross of Canada. At thirteen feet, all three missed their
first attempts. Cross cleared on his second and was
just one jump away from the title, then Price and
Seibert succeeded on their third try.

The vaulting had already taken three hours and was
still undecided. The three remaining competitors had
required almost as much stamina as skill; but now all
seemed weary as they relaxed between jumps.

"They're a tired bunch," an official declared. "Let's
raise the bar to thirteen feet four inches. That should
not only give a winner but will, if cleared, also create a
new Empire record."

Price and Seibert and Cross all jumped in that
order. On the first two tries, each failed. The Aus-
tralian and the South African made valiant attempts on
their third and final jump, but each just ticked the bar
and it tumbled into the pit. Dave was just as weary as
his adversaries. He was ready to settle for a tie rather
than take more jumps at a lower height or to count up
the previous misses and decide on that basis.

However, he struggled to his feet, picked up the pole,
measured the height and strolled leisurely to his starting
position. Then he took a deep breath and suddenly
thought of that telegram from home. "Keep fighting,"
it said. Dave took heart. "Just one more jump," he
thought. "I'll give it everything I've got. This is it."

Instantly, he felt relaxed and refreshed. Quickly he
dashed down the narrow cinder track. He snapped the
pole into the box; the pole seemed to bend as it whipped
him into the air; upwards he kicked his legs; strongly he
pushed the pole away; his body arched; his arms shot

up in the air; his chin just missed the bar as he cleared and tumbled down into the soft earth. Before he landed the cheers of the crowd were roaring through the stadium. Cross had won for Canada at a measured height of thirteen feet three and one-half inches; and a record. His second thought was, "Grandpa will be tickled to know that a Cross still does better in combat."

The Champion Returns Home

CHAPTER 19

When Dave returned home with his British Empire championship and first-place gold medal, his mother and grandfather were keenly interested in his experiences.

Mrs. Cross was very anxious to know about the people he had met, the places he had visited and whether or not he had taken enough clothing with him. His grandfather, too, was interested in that information, but even more he wanted to know about the athletes he had seen and what he learned about pole-vaulting.

"Who was the best athlete at the games?" Mr. Cross inquired.

"That's hard to say, grandpa," Dave believed. "I spent most of my time, of course, around track and field, but there were some great competitors in other sports. There was a sculler from Australia who was so good that the English experts were saying he would win the next Olympics.

"But the Australians are good in so many events," Dave continued. "They had a high-jumper named Summers who cleared six feet seven inches. The same fellow also doubled in the running broad jump and leaped about twenty-four feet; but a Nigerian beat that by about six inches. He sure could jump."

"How about the track events, Dave? How did Canada do?" Mr. Cross inquired.

"We didn't do too badly. We won both the 440 yards and one mile relays, but individually we weren't tops," Dave replied. "In the sprints the English and Australians were the best. In the shorter middle distances, the quarter and the half, the Jamaicans were the winners. My those coloured fellows could travel fast; their times were close to world's records."

"What happened in the longer races, Dave?" Mr. Cross asked.

"Grandpa, the mile race was the finest I ever saw," Dave enthusiastically recalled. "England had three milers entered and all of them had done 4.11 or better. We had two, Jarvis and McFee."

"McFee?" inquired Mr. Cross with a tone of doubt.

"Yes! Chuck McFee," Dave answered. "You probably haven't heard very much about him because he came originally from Quebec and went to a United States university on a scholarship. He did most of his running over there. A very nice fellow; he told me I should go to his school. He told me I would get along

108

all right if I kept up my studies. They wouldn't carry a fellow who didn't pass his exams, even if he broke a world's record."

"But about that mile race, Dave," Mr. Cross asked smilingly. "You seem to be running off your track."

"That's right, grandpa. I was out of my lane, wasn't I?" Dave answered with a grin. "Yes! that mile race. It was featured as the big event of the Games. Well! there were ten starters and right from the gun it was evident that only McFee, Jarvis and the three English runners would be in the battle. Jarvis, a fast starter, broke with the gun, dashed into the lead like a quarter-miler and ran the first lap in fifty-eight seconds. He was then leading by about five yards over a close pack that included 'Chuck' and the three Englishmen."

Dave continued, "In the second lap, the pace slowed just a trifle, somewhere around sixty-one seconds as I recall. Jarvis still set the pace and the rest watched each other just as if they were playing cops and robbers. In the third lap, one of the English runners jumped the field and gained a ten yards lead. Mel Jarvis slipped some. His pace had been pretty hot."

"It sure had, Dave," Mr. Cross interjected. "A 2.01 half is terrific."

"Well! grandpa," Dave continued, "in the third lap, when one English runner was away out in front, the other two caught Jarvis, then hustled around McFee and were running one, two, three."

"That was a difficult spot for the Canadian, Dave," Mr. Cross explained. "I've seen that done in international competition. The Finns are great for teaming and jockeying like that. It means that the other fellow has to run around three men instead of one."

"That's right, grandpa. It was tough for Chuck," Dave agreed. "Every time he challenged, they spurted and spread so that our man had to go wide or drop back. However, Chuck was a smart man, too. He watched the third runner closely and just as the Englishman rounded the corner into the stretch, McFee noted a slight faltering. There was a gap of about four yards. Quickly, Chuck jumped and passed, and slipped into third spot on the rail."

"Smart work," Mr. Cross snapped.

"It was," Dave agreed. "Well! McFee continued his strategy. On the far stretch on the last lap, he again saw a clearance wide enough for him to jump into second place; and he made it. He then continued stride for stride right on the heels of the leader. The two of them rounded the last curve just a yard apart and continued into the stretch. The English runner was noted for his finish. The feeling was that he could beat any miler in the world who didn't have at least three yards' lead when fifty yards from home. But Chuck, too, had a kick and he still had some reserve. He caught his man about ten yards from the tape and as they plunged for the finish line, it was anybody's race. The judges disagreed. They called for a photograph before giving a decision. When the picture was received, it required a microscope to detect that McFee had won by about the thickness of a jersey. Believe me, it was some race," he added.

"What was the time, Dave?" his grandfather eagerly inquired.

"Four minutes and seven seconds. A new Empire record," Dave recalled. "And say, grandpa, when you get a record in England, you really earn it."

"What do you mean, son?" Mr. Cross asked.

"I mean that they make sure the previous record was broken fairly," Dave explained. "For instance, they didn't just take the timers' results and say, 'A new record.' No sir, before they approved the times, they sent all the timers' watches to Greenwich and had them tested for accuracy. Not until they got that report did the officials accept that 4.07 time."

"That's nice, Dave. I like to see justice done to the former recordholder," Mr. Cross remarked. "The English, you know, have a reputation for good sportsmanship."

"And they live up to it, too," Dave added. "They made us feel that we were not strangers, but really members of a big family. Now about my pole-vault, grandpa."

"I wondered when you were going to get around to that, son, but I didn't want to interrupt."

"Well, grandpa," Dave began, "you probably heard about it on the air and read accounts in the papers. I also brought some pictures that show me going over the bar on my last jump. But you better not be too critical about it, for I had then been vaulting for more than three hours and my good old Cross form probably had some flaws.

"It was a good event, grandpa," Dave continued. "Australians and South Africans never give an inch; you have to battle all the way to beat them. I was jumping well, coach."

111

"That thirteen feet three and one-half inches proved that, Dave," Mr. Cross suggested.

"It proved, as you said, sir, that if an athlete's style is sound, he will improve in competition. That's the first lesson I learned," Dave admitted. "And the other one was that pole-vaulting isn't a sissy sport. It's one that demands not only vaulting, but also the utmost in condition. For instance, even the six-mile race was over in about thirty minutes; but I was around the vaulting standards waiting or jumping for almost two hundred minutes. At the end, it was really reserve strength that won for me. That and the telegram from you and mom telling me to 'Keep fighting,'" Dave added.

Sports and Studies Clash

CHAPTER 20

Within a week after his return from England, Dave was back at work, digging post holes for a power company.

"Did you show the other workers your medal, Dave?" Mrs. Cross inquired jokingly as her son returned home one week-end.

"No! mom, I didn't," Dave laughingly replied. "I was afraid I might lose it out of my pocket, and I certainly couldn't pin it on my bare chest."

Dave laboured outdoors until university opened. He had passed his examinations and was enrolled in his second year. The intercollegiate track and field championships were held in early October, and Dave easily won the pole-vault and became entitled to his university letter.

Around the campus he was now a noted student. Girls were taking increasing interest in him; and while he was sociable and friendly, he still reserved his best dates for Mildred Graham, his Park Tech pal.

Dave was a well-balanced youth. He didn't accept other opinions too readily, and he also thought things out very carefully before he made his own important decisions. Whether or not he should join a fraternity was one of those questions still in doubt.

Fraternities had been working hard on him. They were very anxious to become brotherly with a student who starred at both studies and sport. For some time, Dave wasn't sure if fraternities were a good thing. Some of the students thought they were too exclusive; that they were nothing but cliques and that some of the members were snobs. There were also rumours around the campus that the sport directors who had themselves belonged to fraternities gave preference to members of their own fraternity when the football team was named.

Dave agreed those things weren't good; but fraternity members denied them. They, in turn, explained that in fraternities the students made close friends who remained so all their life and helped them in business and social affairs. Fraternity houses also gave them an opportunity to entertain, a quiet room in which to study and a convenient stopping-place on days when lectures were hours apart. "Besides," they told him, "our initiations will be very humbling, and humility and respect are good for a young man."

There was very little doubt that initiates would be humbled. Other students had told Dave that before acceptance they were instructed to carry bricks in a

114

basket on a busy street car; to wear gowns and sing solos on prominent corners; to be left penniless, after midnight, in a distant and strange part of the city and forced to hitch-hike to the fraternity house; to step aside and bow gracefully when they met "brothers"; to scrub floors and paint doors, and paste wall-paper in fraternity homes.

"What should I do, mom. Join or not?" he asked at dinner one evening.

"Dave, there are some decisions you should make for yourself," his mother advised. "This seems to me to be one of them. But if you do join, I think you should pay your own dues. You worked hard all summer; you have saved some money. If you think you would prefer to spend it that way, that will be all right with me."

Dave turned to his grandfather and said, "I don't know, grandpa. I think fraternities are all right, but I'm wondering if I can afford it. What's your opinion?"

Mr. Cross looked at Mrs. Cross, smiled, shrugged his shoulders and remarked, "I'm like your mother. I don't want to influence you unduly. I'll just say this, Dave, 'Don't pay too much for your whistle.'"

Dave considered that remark very carefully. "Don't pay too much for your whistle," he repeated to himself. "I read that story about Benjamin Franklin in one of the school readers. It meant 'Don't buy anything you can't afford.'" He finally concluded that fraternities were all right, but they were probably too costly if he had to work hard with pick and shovel to pay for initiation, dues and the monthly expenses.

During that winter, Dave continued playing hockey with Marlboros. They were a good team. The coach understood that he was available for only home games and that his school examinations were more important than scoring goals. Even on practice days, Dave would get to the Gardens early, sit in a box seat, spread his books beside him, and read without interruption in that huge, quiet arena. At times it seemed strange for him to be studying French literature or economics or history in a rink that at the moment had seats for 15,000 people and only one occupant.

After Marlboros had won their district title and had captured the provincial honour, they played the Quebec champions. The Montreal Royals were a good club and the series continued through six games and both were still tied, with the deciding game to be played in Montreal on a Tuesday night.

"We would like to have you play with us, Dave," the coach proposed. "We missed you in our other Montreal games. I think your presence would have given us the margin we needed to win. When a centre player is replaced, the whole line slumps."

"I have an examination Tuesday morning, coach. It's a final, too, and I couldn't afford to miss it," Dave informed him.

"Well, the team is going down by train on Monday night. I admit you couldn't take that," the coach agreed. "But! there's a plane leaving Tuesday afternoon. It gets to Montreal a couple of hours ahead of game time. How about taking that plane? Then you could leave on the regular train right after the game and be home early Wednesday morning."

116

"That idea seems all right, coach," Dave responded. "You get the tickets and I'll fly down on the afternoon plane."

But on Tuesday morning a blizzard blew up without warning. Snow, sleet and gale were so heavy and strong that planes were grounded and Dave never did reach Montreal Forum. That night, Royals won a close game by four to three and Dave's hockey for that season ended.

When his school term finished, Dave again secured outdoor work. Occasionally, during the summer, he turned out for some sprinting and vaulting, and even competed in a couple of local track meets and won his special event at heights about twelve feet six inches.

But his heart wasn't in the sport. He wasn't keen enough to train steadily.

However, his grandfather suggested, "Don't get too far away from competition, Dave. You never know what could happen. Olympic Games are being held next year at Helsinki. You might like to see Finland— with all expenses paid."

More Professional Hockey Offers

CHAPTER 21

Dave had again passed in all subjects at the university and in the autumn returned for his third year. Again, of course, he played hockey until early in January. Then, one day he received a telegram asking him to have dinner with the managing director of a National Hockey League team.

"I can at least listen to him," Dave told his mother. "I wouldn't, of course, do any signing until the three of us talked it over."

Following the dinner, the hockey manager got down to the real purpose of his visit. "Dave," he began, "my head scout has been watching you play for years. We looked at you even when you played with Westport midgets, and right from the first you impressed us that you were the best lad to come-up in a long time. We knew about your desire for an education and we respected it. But we need players, good ones like yourself, right away. I must admit we are desperate or we wouldn't bother you now. So, I want to make an offer."

Without waiting for any reply from Dave, he continued. "We usually think $5,000 a season is a good start for a rookie. But! in your case we'll do better, much better."

He stopped to see the reaction of Dave, but the young fellow just nodded and listened.

"In your case, Dave," the magnate went on, "we'll make the best offer that we have made in many years. We will pay you $7,500 for your first season."

But Dave didn't give any indication of his feelings. "And that isn't all," the manager added. "My scout tells me that you are very much attached to your grandfather. I like that, son. Family pride is a great thing. I wish more lads had it. Now I understand that you are still a minor and that your grandfather would do the signing of any contract. So, in addition to your salary of $7,500, we would, just as a gesture of our goodwill, make your grandfather a present of $2,500."

"What do you think of that, Dave?" the promoter asked rather abruptly.

"When do you want my answer?" Dave countered.

"Well! Cross, I'd like to know as soon as possible," the hockey magnate replied. "Our club has the reputation for dealing fairly with any young man we contact. We need you and need you badly right now. But you are the one to make the decision. Would you

119

like me to approach your guardian or would you prefer to talk it over with him alone?"

"Better leave it with me," Dave thought. "I'll let you know our decision."

While Dave, his mother and his grandfather were talking over the offer and viewing it from all angles, the problem was further complicated by a cable from Paris.

The Canadian Olympic hockey team was already in Europe and was playing exhibition matches in Oslo, Stockholm, Brussels, Paris and Rome prior to the Olympic series at Chamonix in the French Alps. The Canadians had been winning, but the scores were so close that the Olympic committee felt that their team needed strengthening promptly. So they asked for a defenceman, a centre and a right-wing to be despatched immediately. Cross was the centre they desired, not only because of his ability, but also because he could take the amateur oath. They would require him along with Knox and Kress to fly to Paris within a week.

"It never rains but it pours, grandpa," Dave remarked as he handed over the cable. "It was tough enough to have to decide whether to become a professional hockey player right away, without having to make this Olympic decision. I must admit I don't know what to do."

They discussed the advantages and disadvantages far into the night. It was not one, but two big problems they had to solve. Then, when a solution seemed as far away as ever, Mr. Cross sat up straight and said, "Dave, I have a suggestion. Syl Apps once had to make a decision just like yours. He was a Canadian champion pole-vaulter; he won the Empire Games' title; he

120

attended university and he later played professional hockey. Ask him what he would advise."

"That's a great idea," Dave agreed. "I like it. Syl's experience would help me a whole lot. You call him up tomorrow."

"Oh! no, Dave," his grandfather counselled. "You're a man now. You make your own contact and you make your own decision. Have no fear, Syl Apps is a very fine fellow and a Y.M.C.A. director. He is easily approached and I'm sure will give you good advice."

The following evening Dave called at the Apps' home and, after the usual courtesies, he explained his mission.

"Mr. Apps, I have a real problem, and I think you could help me solve it better than anyone else," Dave started. "On the one side of my problem I have been offered $7,500 a year to play professional hockey, and I have also been asked to fly to Paris and join the Canadian Olympic hockey team. That's one side.

"On the other side," Dave continued. "I'm the holder of the British Empire pole-vaulting title and the Olympic Games are coming up next summer in Finland. In addition, I'm now in my third year Arts Course at the university, and if I pass I will be entitled to my B.A. degree.

"My problem is, Mr. Apps," Dave concluded. "Should I go to Paris, should I sign to play professional hockey, or should I finish my education?"

"How old are you, Dave?" Syl asked.

"I'll be twenty in June," Dave answered.

"That was my age, too," Apps smiled. "I had just the same problem. I figured it out this way. I had

121

already spent about twelve years in public school, high school and university. My mother had spent a lot of money to get me that education. If I had quit in the last year it would have hurt her and it would have prevented me getting my degree. And I had already worked hard and long to get that B.A.

"Then, in addition," Syl continued, "I was young. I still hadn't seen much of the world and I knew it would be a real thrill to visit strange places in Europe. Besides, I liked pole-vaulting and to compete at the Olympic Games would crown my athletic activities. It was a chance that, once declined, would never be repeated. So, I stayed home, studied, passed my exams, kept training for the Olympics, and got there."

Then he added, "When I came back from the Berlin games, I was still twenty, and I signed a professional hockey contract with Mr. Smythe. As I look back, I am satisfied I made the right decision."

Before Dave left Mr. Apps he knew that his counsel had been wise. He thanked his friend, and decided, "The road you chose is good enough for me."

Dave Makes the Olympic Team

Dave continued his studies with new heart. He seemed more satisfied as though a weight had been lifted too from his shoulders. His mother and grandfather were pleased with his decision, for it was the one they too would have made. In June, they were delighted to attend the ceremonies when Dave received his degree from the Chancellor of the University.

At that time, Dave was working in the office of a friendly contractor who knew Dave's plans and allowed him the time to train as he preferred for the Olympic Trials. But even though his plans already included the trip to Finland's capital, he still hadn't succeeded in making the Canadian team. However, he practised diligently and received constant attention from his grandfather.

"You know, Dave," his coach reminded, "the Olympics aren't the British Empire Games. At London, your thirteen feet four inches was a real good mark. It was a fine jump. But it's worth knowing that the Americans, Japs, Swedes and Norwegians weren't there. They are good vaulters; the world's best. I wouldn't be surprised if a fellow had to do better than fourteen feet to even get into the final six at Helsinki."

The Canadian Olympic committee thought so, too, for they decided that only a pole-vaulter who could equal thirteen feet nine inches would be named to the team.

"That's quite a stiff test," Dave told his grandfather. "I win the British Empire championship just under thirteen feet four inches, yet I must climb to thirteen feet nine inches or I miss the Olympic boat."

Mr. Cross explained that it would cost at least $1,200 to send an athlete from Canada to the games and it didn't seem right to spend that money just to give a trip to someone who didn't have a chance.

On the day set for the Canadian trials, Dave was fit in mind and body. Conditions were ideal and performances in most events were excellent. However, in the pole-vault, that standard of thirteen feet nine inches was so high that it had discouraged many ordinary vaulters for no entrants other than Dave had so far exceeded thirteen feet in competition.

As the jumping advanced, it was soon evident that Cross would win. Indeed, other than Dave, only Jamieson from Hamilton, cleared thirteen feet and he missed in his three trials at thirteen feet six inches. Dave cleared thirteen feet six inches and the bar was raised on the uprights to thirteen feet nine inches.

That was the highest that Dave had ever attempted. On that day it would have made a new native Canadian record, and he was determined to do his best. At the moment, however, he was vaulting alone. He had beaten all challengers and, to Dave, that challenge was missing; the urge to beat someone else had gone. He was only competing against some figures on paper; and that wasn't very inspiring.

However, the bar was ready. The height was announced to the crowd and Dave took his turn. He cleared the bar all right but, when descending, his right arm just ticked the cross-piece and it took one turn and slid lazily to the ground. On his second trial he was again over the bar cleanly, but the long bamboo pole swayed and dislodged the bar and, in falling, it broke. A new crossbar was provided.

Dave then asked, as the rules permitted, that the vaulting uprights be moved about two inches closer to the pit. The officials obliged, Dave jumped and cleared. It was the best vault he ever made, and the throng cheered him mightily.

"That equals the standard set by the committee," an official declared. "That means Cross has made the team."

"Better measure it to be sure," a judge advised. "Bob Richards, United States champion, has vaulted higher but that is the best ever for a Canadian. We must be accurate."

Dave donned his sweat suit and cooled-out on the grass, while the measurers climbed a tall ladder and extended a steel tape-line from the lowest point in the crossbar to the ground.

"What do you get?" shouted the recording scorer.

The officials huddled, shook their heads, then one of them walked over to the athlete.

"Too bad, Dave," the official said.

"What's too bad?" Dave asked impatiently. "A new Canadian record can't be too bad. What's the trouble?"

"Just this, Cross," he explained. "The crossbar at the side was set at thirteen feet nine inches, but the new bar we used had quite a sag in the centre. Perhaps the ground, too, was uneven. We had to measure from the lowest point of the bar, and the tape records only thirteen feet eight inches. That is a new mark for a Canadian all right, but it still isn't the height required to make the Olympic team. What do you want to do about it?"

"I'm pretty well cooled-out now," Dave wearily replied. "My muscles feel stiff already. But there's only one thing to do. I'll jump again. Put it up to thirteen feet ten inches to be sure."

Again Dave jumped, but the delay had so tightened him that he could hardly get up with the pole, let alone kick his legs over the bar. Awkwardly, he broke the wood and slumped into the pit.

When he picked himself from the dirt, Dave brushed and shook, then turned to the referee and declared with real disappointment, "I'm through for the day. If I jump again I might break a leg. I'll have to let the committee decide if I make the team."

Immediately following the games the committee was hurriedly assembled. "We have an unusual case before us," the chairman announced. "The facts are that we set the standard for pole-vaulters at thirteen feet nine inches. It was a high mark, although there are a dozen vaulters around the world who can make it. Cross cleared what the officials thought was thirteen feet nine inches, but the tape line proved it was only thirteen feet eight inches. During the delay, Cross cooled-out and his muscles stiffened. Those are the facts. What are your wishes? Should Cross be included on the team?"

"Better stick to our rule," one member believed. "It's too bad that the incident occurred. If the bar had been raised in the first place to thirteen feet ten inches, Cross might have cleared and there would have been no fuss. But! it wasn't, and he didn't."

"If we make an exception in this instance," another member thought, "then we would have to lower our standards in other events. No! I'm in favour of rejection. We can use the $1,200 for some other purpose."

Just then there was a knock on the door and the chairman answered and excused himself from the meeting. "I'll be back in a minute, gentlemen."

When he returned, he said to the members, "Gentlemen, I have a sporting proposition. I'm not so sure that our own officials aren't responsible for Cross not clearing thirteen feet nine inches in the first trial. They should have allowed more margin of safety. However, I'm assured that if Cross does not clear thirteen feet nine inches at Helsinki that a sum covering all his expenses will be returned to the Canadian Olympic Association. Should we accept the offer?"

"It's a deal," one member shouted. They all agreed. The offer was accepted. Dave was at last an Olympian.

Olympic Games
at Helsinki

CHAPTER 23

The Canadian Olympic Team assembled at Montreal and the athletes were promptly allotted berths. Dave's companion was Mel Robb, a university student from Eastern College. Mel was a high-jumper so the two competitors were nicely matched. They had much in common and could train at the same time.

After a couple of exciting days in Montreal, where the uniforms were distributed and the members introduced, the boat steamed out of the old harbour, under great arched bridges, down the St. Lawrence, past Quebec City and Anticosti Island, through the Straits of Belle Isle, out across the ocean to Liverpool.

Fortunately, the ocean, instead of being nasty, was almost as smooth as the water in a swimming tank.

During the voyage there was the usual round of games and parties, with concerts each night in the library. Dave was surprised to learn that so many team members were not only champion athletes but were also noted singers and exceptionally good musicians. Indeed, his room-mate Mel Robb was such an experienced pianist that he had given recitals.

On Sunday morning there was Divine Service on the boat and it was so well attended that many members had to stand.

But! the trip wasn't just a journey to England. It was also the mission of the best athletes in Canada, who were destined to represent their native land in world-wide competition. Every man and woman on the team knew they had been sent at great cost and were determined to do their duty. So, with some sacrifices, they ate carefully and endeavoured to maintain normal weights. But, as usual, boxers, wrestlers and weight-lifters, who were competing in weight classes, found it difficult to avoid adding a few pounds to their finely-trained bodies.

All too soon, it seemed, the boat docked at Liverpool and they were quickly entrained for London. Then from London, instead of taking another long and per-haps rough sea trip to Helsinki, the entire team was transported by plane. From the Finnish airport, the men athletes were promptly motored to Olympic Village.

The Village was a little town in itself. It had many blocks of new three-storey buildings, enough to house about 5,000 athletes. It had its own post-office, chapel, restaurant, stores, cycledrome, immense practice grounds, and a first-class running track. It didn't have just one of anything, for the big field included two of each kind of jumping areas, and up to six places each for practicing in hammer, discus, shot and javelin.

The building set apart for meals had over sixty dining-rooms, a separate one for each country. In each, the athletes were fed the same kinds of food they had enjoyed back home. That was very important, for strange dishes could so upset a competitor that he might become ill just at the hour when his best effort was demanded. Champions have been beaten by a piece of pie. Drinking water was also so important that some national teams had transported their own supply.

At this huge training ground, which was only a couple of miles from the real Olympic stadium, Dave was amazed at the harmony and friendliness. Coaches from one country quickly gave help to athletes from another. Competitors from many nations shared the same equipment and respected each other's training hours. Men who couldn't understand one another's language nodded and smiled as they met. At one time, Dave counted six sprinters, each from a different country, practicing starts while a Finnish official gave the commands in his native tongue.

So friendly was the feeling that Dave trained for his pole-vaulting with the Americans who were undoubtedly the world's best in that event. They loaned him their poles, showed him their styles and encouraged the Canadian as though he was a member of their own team.

One morning, the United States' head coach came over to the vaulting area, walked up to Dave and remarked, "They tell me you are from Canada and your name is Cross. Was your grandfather a sprinter?"

"Yes sir, he was," Dave replied.

"Well! when you get back," the coach laughed, "tell the old boy that you met Tom Conley, and you can add that Cross never saw the day he could beat me." Dave promised.

While all the nations were showing peace and good-will during the practice days, it was evident that athletes were becoming more anxious as the actual competition neared.

The opening ceremonies themselves were thrilling and impressive. An hour before the set time, the competitors from Olympic Village, garbed in their colourful ceremonial dress, began arriving at the parade ground outside the huge stadium. Soon they formed into long lines, each country headed by a carrier bearing the country name and a flag-bearer carrying the national flag.

With a loud fanfare of trumpets, the army of athletes began marching through a tunnel into the vast stadium and on the track. The nations marched in alphabetical order, except that Greece was given the place of honour as a tribute to the fact that Olympic Games originated in that country; and the Finnish team, as hosts, were the last to enter the stadium. The athletes paraded past the Loge of Honour, saluted in their own national way, then rounded the track, turned to the playing area and lined-up facing the distinguished guests. They filled the entire grass infield; and in the bright afternoon sun, with a faint breeze blowing the

131

sixty national flags, the scene was one of hope and beauty. It was a moment when the whole world seemed to be at ease.

There was a brief pause, then a well-trained voice spoke clearly throughout the stadium, "The important thing in the Olympic Games is not winning but taking part. The essential thing in life is not conquering but fighting well."

After a brief address of welcome, the President of Finland declared, "I proclaim the games at Helsinki, in celebration of the fifteenth Olympiad of the modern era, open."

Instantly, there was action. The white Olympic flag bearing five different coloured circles was hoisted at the main mast. Artillery salute boomed from the parade ground. Thousands of pigeons were released and formed a cloud as they whirled in all directions to carry messages of goodwill to their home cities. There were more trumpet fanfares, then the entire throng of 60,000 men and women stood respectfully while a robed choir and a 100-piece orchestra sang and played the Olympic hymn. Then a torch-bearer entered the stadium, circled the track, climbed the steps to the Olympic altar, plunged the torch into a large copper bowl, and the Olympic fire was lighted.

Later, while the flag-bearers formed a half-circle in front of the Loge of Honour, their national colours dipped when a Finnish athlete raised his right hand in salute and repeated for all athletes, "We swear that we will take part in the Olympic games in loyal competition, respecting the regulations which govern them, and desirous of participating in them in the true spirit of sportsmanship for the honour of our country and for the glory of sport."

With the singing of the Hallelujah Chorus by the massed choir, the opening ceremonies ended; the athletes trooped from the stadium and returned to the village to rest for the games that would come on the morrow.

Cross –
Canada –
Third

CHAPTER 24

On the morning of the second day of the games, all pole-vaulters were instructed to appear at the stadium for their qualifying round. The purpose of this was to ensure that all competitors were worthy, also that there wouldn't be too many participants in the actual competition.

The minimum height expected from each vaulter was equivalent to about twelve feet six inches. Even then there were some eliminated; but Dave had no trouble clearing and was declared eligible for the real contest which was to be held on the afternoon of the next day.

It was one of the big days of the games. The programme included the semi-finals and finals of the women's 100 metres race; the heats of the men's 200 metres; the final of 800 metres; the heats of the 5,000 metres; the discus, and the pole-vault.

When the vaulting began there were twenty-five qualifiers. They were almost a League of Nations for they included athletes from Canada, Great Britain, United States, Japan, West Germany, Russia, Austria, Hungary, South Africa, Czechoslovakia, Italy, Poland, Sweden, France, Denmark, and Chile.

When Dave battled with these competitors he was well aware that this was "The Day," the one for which he had remained an amateur through all his playing years, the one for which he had sacrificed many hundreds of hours. It was the chance of a lifetime and he was determined to do his utmost to bring credit to his country, his grandfather and himself. However, he had no illusions about beating the Americans. Two of them had cleared fifteen feet several times. So every other competitor left them out of their reckoning.

As Dave sat on the ground awaiting his turn, the 5,000-metre runners were swiftly striding around the red, brick-dust track. Many tens of thousands of Finns and their guests from foreign lands were crowded into the stadium, intently and expertly observing every athlete. Around the top of the stands the flags of all nations were fluttering lazily, and high above, the cloudless blue sky provided a flawless canopy. "Win or lose," Dave thought, "it's quite a sight. I'm glad I made it."

Suddenly he heard, "Cross, Canada." At once his competitive spirit was aroused. He arose, picked up his pole, measured the height for his hand grips, jogged to

135

his starting mark, took a long breath, crouched, ran, increased his speed, jabbed the pole-end in the box, climbed with the pole, kicked his legs, hard and high, pushed the pole away, arched his body over the bar, straightened his arms as he dropped, then rolled into the soft earth. The height was only about twelve feet six inches, but Dave had felt right. One of the Americans came over to him and said, "Nice style, pal. You'll go a long way."

The bar was raised about six inches to thirteen feet, and seventeen cleared. It was upped to thirteen feet six inches and eleven were still in.

When the bar was lifted to fourteen feet, Dave had a distressing moment. He knew that it had been his grandfather who had promised to pay the Canadian Olympic Committee all the expenses of the journey if Dave failed to clear their standard of thirteen feet nine inches. This fourteen feet was the one height he just had to make. There could be no failure at this spot, even though it was the highest he had ever gone.

When "Cross" was again called, Dave smiled hopefully to his American friends, "Remember, Canada, take a higher grip on the pole," one of them hollered.

Dave measured, placed his hands on the spots that seemed usual for him. Then, looking around, he saw his friend motioning about another four inches and Dave gripped higher. He climbed, cleared, rolled in the Finnish soil; then grinned and waved at his California friend.

When the bar was raised to fourteen feet seven inches, only the two Americans, a Jap, a Swede, a Russian and the Canadian remained; but only the two

United States vaulters cleared and they continued until one of them created a new Olympic record of fifteen feet three inches.

But! third place was still undecided, so the officials lowered the bar to fourteen feet four inches and instructed the other four to fight it out for the position. The Jap and the Russian failed in their three tries. Gustafson of Sweden and Cross of Canada cleared.

The bar was raised again to fourteen feet seven inches. Both vaulters had been competing over three hours and they were almost exhausted. The Swede jumped first and missed. Dave tried and failed. The Swede again knocked off the bar.

"Get those hands still higher," again shouted the American who had won.

Dave smiled, felt relaxed and gripped again. With a summoning of all his reserves, he cleared the bar, just ticked it with a finger as he descended, then watched the little wooden bar sway but still stick. Gustafson, tired but game, tried again but couldn't quite make it. Dave had won the place.

Track Ends
and Hockey
Starts

CHAPTER 25

A couple of minutes later trumpets were blown and the huge crowd stood at attention. The two Americans and the Canadian mounted the draped dais reserved for champions. Two American flags and the Canadian Ensign were raised on central masts. Over the loud speakers came the announcement, "The pole-vault. First—Nichols, United States. Second—Stinson, United States. Third—Cross, Canada."

The band played "The Star-Spangled Banner" in honour of the winner and his country. A laurel wreath and an Olympic medal was presented to each of the three athletes. The crowd cheered mightily, and Dave was content.

138

Back home in Canada Grandfather Cross turned off the radio, smiled at his daughter-in-law, then turned to his old friend and chuckled as he teased, "You know, Jack, I still think Dave could have been a great weight-thrower."

"Or maybe a miler," Jack laughed.

They both agreed that young Dave had a good mind, a strong body and a fighting spirit that would make him a champion in the more important game of life. Dave at last was ready for professional hockey.

CANADA'S OLYMPIC CHAMPIONS

Summer Sports

1904—St. Louis—Canada—Lacrosse
          E. Desmarteau—56-pound Weight
          G. S. Lyon—Golf

1906—Athens—W. J. Sherring—Marathon

1908—London—R. Kerr—200 Metres Run
          W. H. Ewing—Clay Bird Shooting

1912—Stockholm—G. Goulding—10,000 Metres Walk
          G. R. Hodgson—400 Metres Swim
          G. R. Hodgson—1,500 Metres Swim

1920—Antwerp—E. J. Thompson—110 Metres hurdles
          Schneider—Welterweight Boxing

1928—Amsterdam—P. Williams—100 Metres Run
          P. Williams—200 Metres Run
          E. Catherwood—Women's High
             Jump
          Canada   Women's 400 Metres
             Relay—F. Rosenfeld, E.
             Smith, J. Bell, M. Cook.

1932—Los Angeles—D. McNaughton—Running High
             Jump
          H. Gwynne—Bantamweight Box-
             ing

1936—Berlin—F. Amyot—1,000 Metres Canoe—Single

1920—Canada—Ice Hockey
1924—Canada—Ice Hockey
1928—Canada—Ice Hockey
1932—Canada—Ice Hockey
1948—Canada—Ice Hockey
      Barbara Ann Scott—Figure Skating—Women's